FALLING

IS

LIKE

FLYING

This is a story she never wanted to tell, but in the end she had no choice. When her older sister dies at the age of sixty-nine, it brings back a past the author thought she had left behind. Incensed, she delves back into her childhood, recreating the abusive world that she grew up in, ruled over by her tyrannical father, The Minotaur.

In a narrative by turns shockingly dark and strangely beautiful, she retraces her path through the phantasmagorical labyrinth, bringing a tale of silent trauma to a triumphant, raucous conclusion. Falling is Like Flying is an extraordinary autobiographical story of abuse and resilience, a literary triumph that reminds us what language is capable of.

FALLING

IS

Manon Uphoff

LIKE

Translated from the Dutch by Sam Garrett

FLYING

PUSHKIN PRESS

Pushkin Press
71–75 Shelton Street
London WC2H 9JQ

Falling is Like Flying was first published as *Vallen is als vliegen* by Querido in Amsterdam, 2019

First published by Pushkin Press in 2021

N **ederlands**
letterenfonds
dutch foundation
for literature

This publication has been made possible with financial
support from the Dutch Foundation for Literature

1 3 5 7 9 8 6 4 2

ISBN 13: 978-1-782277-03-3

Typeset by Hewer Text UK Ltd, Edinburgh

Printed and bound by CPI Group (UK) Ltd, Croydon, CR0 4YY

www.pushkinpress.com

For the dead
H.R.
E.U

For the living
T.R., J.M.U., A.M.U., M.M.U., F.U.,
I.M.
Z.B.

And for the souls of
P.E.H.U.
A.U.S.

We must grasp things in the highest sense,
And let what may come, come, with confidence.
You've shown the highest courage once before.
So now too what is fearful, we must try it:
World, and posterity, will stubbornly deny it,
So pen it faithfully in your report.

Faust, Act 1, scene 3

CONTENTS

THE LONG WINTER OF OUR DISCONTENT

R EADER,
I didn't want to tell this story. For a long time I clung
to the idea of my wondrous escape, my "quantum leap",
in the hope of living calmly and collectedly in a world of
fiction. A world of my own making, one I could enter and
leave at will.

As far back as my memory reaches, I have had a love of
stories and a yearning for the telling of them with a hunger
that went far beyond the normal, everyday, and with a
special eye, ear and nose for tragedy. Pawing and chafing
like a horse ... inquisitive, eager. At last something was
happening, at last things were being clarified! Bible stories,
myths, sagas, gruesome fairy tales. They prodded my heart
and prickled my senses. Look there, a hand pierced by nails,
a child with a splinter of ice in his heart, a city destroyed for
its transgressions. How hideous, how grave, how real.

I knew no greater desire than one day to be allowed to
add something to this great edifice of human experience.
But who can predict what will free itself from the darkness
one day to chase us, like a frightened dog?

This love of stories that had warmed me till then I lost in the winter of 2009, and in its place came restlessness.

It was shortly after the publication of a book in which I had portrayed friends, family and also my husband, Oleg. He had turned down flatly the role of muse, and we had entered into a deep crisis. During that same period my best friend let me know that he was incurably ill and that we would not be seeing each other often, and certainly not without worries.

Winter, in other words. Darkness was falling and I stood at the window of my office in the "cottage in the woods" where we had taken up temporary residence, a house over which Oleg had been hired to act as caretaker. An imbalanced and ugly building, lacking all personality, a cheap replacement for the farmhouse that had once marked the property (only the stables were left standing); you could rightly have claimed, therefore, that we were the only authentic objects in it.

Ever since my Shitty Book, my Mean Book, my Bad Book, my work "without morality or conscience", I had hardly worked at all.

The weeks that went before had been harsh. With days on end of accusations, bitter silences, cruel comments and my crying fits, permeated with a stifling self-pity. After which I tried to heal myself by watching *National Geographic* documentaries and taking long walks in the snow, which had gone on falling profusely throughout that period.

Bountiful, bountiful snow. In such huge quantities that I forgot what to do with it, once I had already made snowmen, stuck out my tongue to catch the flakes and watched our young tom, Yevgeni, retrace his own pawprints across the white field. Flake after flake after flake . . . drifted up into towers before the house. And no one to talk to since I had stopped writing, except for letters to my dying friend, but I talked to no one about those letters. One person at least who enjoys hearing from me and receiving reports from my Nova Zembla, I thought. For a Nova Zembla is what it was, and I was on rations almost too skimpy for sustenance. Oleg allowed me to share his bed, it's true, but it was chilly as the tundra. I would leave it in the middle of the night and slip into the room across the hall. My study, ha ha, where I studied nothing at all, only sat on the pine-plank floor he had laid a few months earlier (when we still dreamt of what this place could be), snot and slime running from my nose, naked like a dwarf or an antique Chinese Buddha, tearing one page after the other out of the book. Whole chapters I ripped from the little monster I had created myself, even clumps of hair from my own head, until my wrists throbbed with pain.

What had writing brought me (I asked myself) beside a loss of warmth, care and tenderness?

How hard I tried to defend myself!

Even the cartoonist who drew my portrait for a magazine had given me murky little eyes, no light in the pupils, as though I were some inhuman thing. And I felt nothing of love, not a morsel of pleasure for the pitiful little writer, not even enough money to get by.

And nothing left of the once-so-mesmerizing smell of books, of the pleasure and enjoyment of writing.

'*Per aspera ad astra* . . . you've betrayed me, betrayed . . .'

Oleg's words went on wrenching. You're a cheat. You mingle with others, with your friends and family, but under your arm, or in a shadowy recess, crevice or crack, you're hiding your ratty little notebook . . . Like some creepy-crawly, some über-bitch, you sneak through the corridors of the world we share. (*There's a killer on the road, his brain is squirming like a toad.*)

You see, I'd alienated everyone. And the ones who weren't already alienated were dead.

Bereavement, in other words, and pain and self-castigation, and the intense ripping and shredding of the books. Thirty-two copies and one to go. With me feeling like one of Henry VIII's condemned wives.

King Henry, to six wives
He was wedded.
One died,
One survived,
Two divorced,
Two beheaded.

Lonely and bitter are the aggrieved.

The Sméagol-ish creature in that study? That was me, standing at the window on the final day of the year, looking out at the branches swaying on the trees and two dark figures. Oleg, slim and erect, planting the torches he'd made along both sides of the path, and my ten-year-older brother Max, poking a stick into the fire basket (delighted, as I always am too, to be close to the fire and see how it grew and wavered as it nibbled on itself).

Yes, restlessness, from the moment my youngest sister Libby called to say they wouldn't be coming to celebrate New Year's with us that evening; there had been an accident with the fireworks they'd bought, and she and her wife had to take their young son to the hospital. As she spoke, I listened to the ruffling of my heart at the start of what I now view as the long winter of our discontent. When all of us in the family became patients, suffering from vague disorders and complex symptoms. While I went on living in the house at the forest's edge that was not a house at all, more like a hiding place, a refuge amid the trees, where I cowered the way the little rabbits did from Yevgeni the cat. But he flushed them effortlessly from the bushes. Through the cat flap he dragged them inside, gobbled them down calmly in the front hall and left the lucky rabbit's foot for us. Or an inedible chunk of intestine. In the morning Oleg was the first to step on to the killing floor, and with the bottle of Cillit Bang did his best

5

to make it look like the entrance to a home. But a home it was not, *vide supra*.

A time when all ties were sundered, all promises of loyalty broken. When Libby was on the pills ('Slip me one little Diazepam, one more little Diazepam, oh!') and her wife, Dana Kidd (who had lain in other beds, in other houses), sat at the table during Christmas dinner with a black eye.

And when my brother Max moved into my study, where he slept from New Year's on in a narrow, spare bed. After more than twenty-five years, he had been made redundant at work and in his marriage. His wife had traded him in for a dog-trainer.

He arrived on a Sunday evening, his face covered in the psoriasis which my mother's genes had passed on with mathematical precision to her second, fourth and eighth children. A disorder that waned as the sun peeled off layer after layer, but that in times of adversity ('Who would want me now . . .! I'm fifty-nine already!') swelled glowingly into a scarlet mask with flakes of silver that sometimes blanketed even his eyelids and brought on nasty infections. Without complaint, he slid his briefcase (toothbrush, laptop, underwear) and telescope case up against the pitched wall and lay down on the cot.

In the morning I woke him with a mug of instant coffee, and felt warm and motherly for a moment, but otherwise I never entered the room—even though, at first, I had enjoyed sitting in that sparingly lit space, which I had furnished with a dark wooden table on curved Louis Quinze legs (picked up at the Emmaus), with a white spotlight as reading lamp and an office chair from IKEA, looking out over the conifers on the patch of ground before the house. Delimited on one side and shut off from the world by the secondary road, over which the cars in late afternoon traced their red or amber streamers, tires hissing when the asphalt was damp or wet; on the other side by the hedgerows and spruce trees that formed the entryway to the woods. And to feel calm, content or simply somewhat pleasantly lonesome. (Even though I wasn't, at least not yet.)

A time when I didn't write, yet felt the physical need to surround myself with books, ordered in large numbers from Amazon and Bol.com, while Oleg buckled down to making his own little greenhouse in which he raised chard (*blitva*), tomatoes, radishes and lettuce. And when Libby phoned and phoned. To say that this time her heart had really been used as kitty litter . . . Really nailed to the wall this time with a rusty spike . . .

In the course of which I kept on seeing the way she'd sat on the floor in the middle of our room after Christmas dinner, covered in the ashes of her wrecked marriage. Wringing her hands, her face hollow, her mouth the black hole of a Noh mask. In front of the dining table across which Oleg and I had tossed lit tea-warmers at each other, leaving teary welts across the scarlet distempered wall (ambiance!) and the two Japanese woodblock prints. 'How could she, the conniving bitch! Lying and cheating on me, both at the same time!'

When I thought that none of it would ever change, Oleg snarling at me and Libby calling to say: 'I actually saw her, Dana Kidd . . . at that house . . . her car, she was there, with that person.' Or that my cell phone would vibrate in the middle of the night: 'I've been thinking about it; I don't think she deserves to live . . .!'

When my good friend died, after which the game of chess he and Oleg had been playing remained unfinished atop the piano. And the tall grey wall cabinets, slapped together in a hurry, filled themselves with books, but I wrote nothing more, except (melodramatic) journal entries and Herring Songs, which I posted on Facebook.

Songs for Herring
Once upon a morning
a herring came along
silent, silken, shy
on to the shore it came
wearing a suitcase
tied around its slender waist
a sorrowful expression on its

fishy face
something tender and
melancholic in its, yet manly,
gaze.
'I seek for shelter,' muttered he,
his voice sounding rather soft,
'a house or an apartment, a
private space, a loft,
I am a wealthy fish and I am
willing to pay,
as long as you can offer me a
safe & silent place to stay.'
'Well, come along,' I said,
'Come along with me,
if you are able, if you can,
I have been lonely and
For a while
I have been searching
for a man.'
'I am no man, but fish,' he said
in a friendly voice,
'Well, in that case, you gentle fish,
you leave me no other choice
You can be my tender dish,
and we'll be intimate that way,
rest in my mouth, sweet fish.'
Oh, he tasted good, he tasted,

and, oh, I had been lonely, I, and now it seemed a bitter
waste,
that I had spent a good &
honest being
with my greedy haste & taste.
And now I walk
lonely to the shore
cause silver slender fish like
that come only once
and nevermore . . .
Yes, I should have known
much better
than to mistake him for a dish
and I weep bitter, bitter tears
for my tender fish.
I had spent my fish.

So that, looking back on it now, it all seems to have played
itself out in one long, single season in which each of us
became harder, more stringent and less friendly, while the
snow fell on us thick and bonded as dough and the Great
Recession howled for our livers, kidneys and hearts.

In fact, though, the whole country was on tenterhooks,
shifting hither and thither. Grievances ignited quickly were
shared hurriedly and en masse, then died away, leaving
nothing on the surface but the red paper tatters of fizzled-
out fireworks, a great danger for those sifting the remains

for that which had not yet been detonated. Some events caused a shudder, a communal moment of shock and worry, but those shocks too wore thin quickly enough, became tiring once the moment itself had passed. You grew used to it, while you shifted from one mood to the next and glared at each other, squinting like gunslingers, suspecting in the other a shrewdness you disowned in yourself.

The only distraction was an impromptu visit from our last remaining family friend, Sebastiaan the Silver Surfer (for whom no more room will be set aside here), elderly linguist emeritus, who came cycling out of the woods at a clip, bent low over the handlebars, preceded by his little heralds, the rabbits, racing off on either side of his tyres. He brought us a plastic bag filled with gifts. DVDs and self-published books of poetry and slender works of prose, which he handed me in courtly fashion, with both hands, and which I put aside unread and only came back to years later.

Excuse me for going on about myself for so long. I feel as though I need to tell you what I was and what I wanted to be, before descending step by step to the first place I ever lived. Of which I was reminded in those cheerless days when the beat of an old, familiar drum grew louder and louder.

Yes, turmoil, and alarum . . . and then ignition.

HENNE FIRE

O N 13TH NOVEMBER in the year 2015, Henne Fire
fell down the stairs and died, a few hours before a
group of young people, out on the town at the Bataclan in
Paris, were permanently cut off from all further innocent
outings.

Henne Fire was my sister. My mother's firstborn.

She lay at the bottom of the stairs and refused the
ambulance. This despite the urging of the doctor and
paramedics to have herself admitted to the hospital, seeing
as she was badly malnourished and dehydrated.

It had been years since I'd visited her, I didn't even
know her address. In my life she had become little more
than a recurring moment of ridicule at our annual Family
Day of the Dead. Just look at them: always with that
grown-up son of hers in his chukka-chukka-whoo-whoo
mobility cart. Mother and son, didn't it remind you of
some scene out of *Psycho*? What a bizarre, unbelievable
pair!

Henne Fire was sixty-nine when she fell. No spring
chicken and certainly not, in the words of my father (who

had been dead for fourteen years by then), 'in the full flush of youth'. Since the turn of the century she had led a shadowy existence in her newly built, grout-hazed, two-bedroom bungalow. Housing for seniors at the edge of Nieuwegein, a satellite community built once upon a time by way of dreamland. A suburban landscape where our mother took refuge (with us) in the mid-1970s, a place *sans* violence or pain, with lawns as green as those in *Blue Velvet*.

When I saw Henne after her hapless fall she looked like a bird, her bony nose jutting up, her hands like claws. She was wearing a green dress.

My sister, I hasten to say, was of no economic importance and had not contributed to the national economy for years. Her legacy consisted of a bank account with a few hundred euros in it, some (dance) outfits, porcelain figurines, a smattering of furniture, and an ashtray filled with Pall Mall and Belinda butts. The house was cleared in a morning. Even the physical space she occupied had been cut to a minimum.

In my youth, Henne Fire (sixteen years my senior) had been the consummate symbol of femininity. A magpie, mad about all that glistered, her bouffant hair decked out with headbands. Along with her sister Toddie (one year younger than she) and our mother, they formed a bastion: the Holy Trinity of Smoke. When we, the youngest children, came home from school we would find them ensconced in their palace of nicotine, while the back room swarmed with children of their own, our nephews and nieces. On days when we had school on Utrecht's Schimmelplein, my younger brother Kaj and I would spend our lunch breaks at Henne's. She made porridge for us. 'Want an apple?' she would say, poking one inflated cheek with her index finger. 'Pop! There it goes!'

In the summer she wore her bikini as she made our sandwiches. When she was done, she would stretch out in an orange canvas folding chair that barely fitted in the little mossy-, mouldy-smelling quadrangle, looking like an exile from Naples to this clammy land.

I know, almost for a fact, that in her youth Henne was never regarded as more than "pretty to look at", just like Toddiewoddie. In a certain sense, my mother—after being thrown out of her first husband's home—had brought them to her new marriage like two offerings of fruit. When my parents married in the late 1950s, Henne was five, Toddiewoddie was four. My father, HEHH, Henri Elias Henrikus Holbein, amateur painter, unsuccessful seminarian, believer and (former) jailbird, became their stepfather, years before he ultimately sired us—the youngest, the afterthoughts—and worked his way up with night-school classes to become a mathematician, scientist, statistician; a respected citizen and *pater familias* with an excellent job.

He was, by the same token, a troubled, deeply damaged man (I am able and dare to say now) with terrible tempers, who found an inappropriate outlet for his emotions and desires, pain and humiliation in his (step)daughters.

My father grew up during the Great Depression that followed the First World War, in a family not averse to fascist sympathies and ideologies. Although no clear commitment was ever made, some imprint concerning lives that matter and lives that don't must have lingered in his thinking. He was extremely particular about women. They represented bodies, beauty and the safety he sought. HEHH missed having a warm mother, and was devoted to the Virgin Mary in a way that drove us to despair. His eyes glistened with emotion when he talked about the miracle: how she had come into the world free of original sin, gave birth to Jesus *and* remained a virgin.

We, the children of the house, were his. He dressed us, fed us, earned his money for us, ignored us. Once he had reached a ripe old age, Henne cared for him kindly. All things considered, HEHH died in relative peace. Not at all like Henne Fire. At the time of his death, she was the same age I am now. Divorced already, but her son not yet an invalid. Skinny, but not frighteningly emaciated. A pretty woman who dyed her hair the blackest of blacks. On occasion she lost her voice. Weeks went by during which she barely produced a sound, yet no one missed her voice, although at such times we were also denied her laugh, which I can remember now that I think about it.

Leaning forward, hands on her knees, it was a deep sound. Whatever the case, she took care of HEHH during his last years and she was proud of that. I suppose she felt he should be allowed his dignity.

Henne would not appreciate my mentioning her or my writing this.

'I'm not afraid of anyone,' she said, and locked herself away in her house. And, proudly: 'I've always done everything absolutely on my own.'

It was Henne Fire who gave me my first bra. I was twelve at the time, and tried it on beneath the hanging lamp in my brand-new bedroom. She had helped my mother to pick out the wallpaper and the carpet: cheerful 1970s colours, orange and purple (we were going to start a new life), and she handed me the nocturnal-blue wonder for which I had no breasts yet. After her divorce—her husband had been keeping a girlfriend on the side—her income bottomed out. She had no education, no one had ever found that necessary, and she moved to a house to live in alone, the one where she later cared for her son. There was a story that went with that. Our nephew only became handicapped in Henne's home. He had returned to it as an adult, depressive after his own divorce and in need of maternal care. He had neither gainful employment nor a pleasant personality—although the cerebral infarct did change the latter. The thrombosis came after he had spent months lying motionless in his bed on the second floor. Then came a loud bonk, and she found him lying between bed and wall. A canned peach, we called him after that, all soft and sweet. She pushed him up the stairs each evening, step by step.

He grew rounder and fleshier while Henne grew steadily thinner. And thin was something she had always been. The kind of thin someone like Trump is fond of. You know, not too much meat on a woman, except for a pair of jiggly tits, never taking up too much space, never making too much noise.

Rage, sometimes I have the feeling it will never be extinguished, that it burns on as an eternal flame. A few years after her son moved in, her welfare allowance was cut; after all, she could now share her household affluence with her son, who felt in no way obligated to contribute a single euro to the cause. He took his meals elsewhere. At a Van der Valk restaurant. He drove there in his mobility cart, and never skipped dessert.

We gossiped about that when we heard.

Henne Fire said nothing. She was capable of formidable silences.

She was silent about HEHH, who must have visited her too as a girl in his guise as Minotaur. And about her natural father, who had once asked Toddie to show him her panties.

She just went on smoking like a chimney and eating less and less.

She laughed loudly, went on with her dancing for a few years after her divorce, and persisted in her silence with a light, secretive smile playing about her lips.

She was old, I *figured* she was old. She was poor, single, had no job.

She was my living, breathing nightmare.

'Please, dear Lord, don't let me turn out like Henne.'

She could laugh like a hyena. But she wasn't a witch, not the way the neighbourhood children shouted after her.

She was solitary, tight-lipped.

Isn't that fine and as it should be? Who, after all, cares for a hysteric? A spiteful woman?

On the night she died, ninety young people were mowed down at the Bataclan, and I didn't dare admit to the horror of her unpretentious death

Now I'm standing with a bunch of white roses beside her purple gypsy grave, so small and narrow, and, oh, founding fathers, my rage blazes high enough to heat the world.

'Grab 'em by the pussy.'

Give them all the sack.

Let them take care of their pissy-smelling parents, their children.

Stick a dick in 'em.

I can feel my anger grow, waxing multiform as a scene by Hieronymus Bosch. Calm down. Become the mistress of your own words. Look at your rage, the orange and gold, the cool blue. That's the point where it's hottest, where you can melt iron with it . . .

Henne Fire stoked hers on the inside, like a chunk of bitumen. The last time I'd wanted to be like her was in 1975, right after I got that bra.

After that I must have taken off running.

True, there had been unpleasant and dramatic events aplenty within our family and circle of friends as from 2008/2009, that long winter of our discontent. At the same time, in the public arena, I as a writer had felt the repercussions of the deputy minister's verdict that my art, in fact all art, was merely a "left-wing hobby". Yet it was not until 2015, I believe, that we "young 'uns" realized that we had not exactly chiselled our names in granite either, and that we were, after a certain fashion, made up of a multitude of impossibilities. My foreign husband Oleg, the economic dropouts in our family, the mentally handicapped brother, the sick brother who didn't dare to stay home for fear of losing his job and out of dread for the prying eyes of the medical insurance company, me with my mouth full of dental implants that turned out to have been implanted by a quack, and then poor, lonely Toddiewoddie, without a man but with a purple bunny-vibrator, weeping for the loss of her sister.

That is to say, all of us: the misfits, the oddballs.

I did not see Henne often, I saw her only rarely—that one day in the year when we met to commemorate HEHH at a restaurant in Nieuwegein.

'If you don't eat, you know what will happen,' I said.

Those were the last words I spoke to my sister.

She smiled at me, her enigmatic smile, and left her soup untouched. Her intake had been dwindling for years. So we worried, but then in a hurried, irritated fashion. We had our own disappointments to deal with, you know what I mean? I, for one, didn't enjoy being called a social parasite.

'Eat, goddamn it, if you don't eat, you're going to die.'

By then we had already stopped trying to tell her that she would find a job, that she would start earning money soon, meet some man, start a new life.

And what's more, we weren't particularly overjoyed about our nephew and that whole situation.

Henne Fire waited until she turned sixty-eight for what she had coming. I think she realized then that it was not going to come.

I barely talked to others about my sister's death. Not with friends. Not with fellow writers.

Shame.

Besides, what could Henne possibly mean to them? I hadn't gone to see her myself for years, for Christ's sake! Like with Scrooge, she was to me a ghost of the past, a phantom I could do without. A memory to avoid. Scorched, burnt out, a harpy.

Still, I dreamt about her. Her hair blowing in the wind, she was perched on a bare branch at the top of a tree.

'Shoo!'

I tried to make her fly away.

Henne Fire, of course, is not her real name. It's the one Isaac Bashevis Singer gave to one of his tremendous characters-in-a-fiery-rage, and I call her that because that is what she did, ignite a flame. On 13th November she knocked sparks like a matchhead off every step on her way down those stairs.

Yes, Henne Fire fell down the stairs, and although the writer in me applied all her energies to keeping this story down—I believe that I even tried to strangle it, to squeeze the breath out of it with my bare hands—I have no choice but to turn back to a history I thought I'd outrun, one that was never mine alone but belonged to all of us. As though we are the roots of one and the same plant, a single, meandrous being.

I am, you see, one of the Holbein children.

Daughter of Henri Elias Henrikus Holbein.

Brilliant architect of our dread and excitement, grand master and auteur of our moments of extreme rapture and fear.

STAGE AND SETTING

E VEN AS A child, I was amazed by the winding vein of
pain and violence that ran through the life of our
family. From the birds that plucked each other bare in the
cage belonging to our older brother Ninny (so that beneath
their bumpy skin we could see the little kidney beans of
their pattering hearts) to the various concoctions and
eruptions full odour, colour and contrast that stored themselves in our childish brains as *tableaux vivants*. Glorious
little glass bubbles fixed in our family memory, which even
today can burst open powerfully within and demand from
me, the family's self-appointed filing clerk, that the shards
be incorporated into new narratives and constellations. So
that I, to paraphrase Nabokov, can rid myself of the
burden of my overabundance.

There was a certain abandonment to the fear. Both in
the causing of it and in its endurance.

During games in the dark, for example. Hide and seek
in pitch-blackness, our mother Anna Alida staying downstairs, smoking in the unlit house, and HEHH tracking us
in the dark, slamming his hands against every step of the

stairs. We, the three youngest (Kaj, Libby and I), always hiding in the same spot: the dust-bunny-infested corner behind Ninny's bed. The first one tagged would die. There was a nocturnal shuffling in the hallway, snorts, sobs, growls . . .

Ninny's rituals: one step forward, two steps backward. His counter-charms: pounding his chest with his fists, biting himself hard on the forearm. He proudly showed us the toothmarks, fiery red against the white flesh. ('Look here, a good one, huh? I made it myself.') There were Henri's maxims ('Vanitas, vanitatum, omnia vanitas', '*How, across the burning, blind basalt, to find my way to Lethe? Oh to forget the one, the all, ere evening falls!*'), and his thumbs pressing hard against the sides of our skulls as he told us about the weakest points on the human body, the temples. But no matter how I pondered and mulled it over, it was all part of that brand of amazement you foster as a child, part of your need to get to know the world. The way one is perfectly able to mull over the action and behaviour taking place on a stage, without necessarily thinking about the concepts of "stage" or "action" themselves.

In addition to which, I was groomed for a life within the framework of the imagination. Born in 1962, during the icy December of a legendarily harsh winter ("The whole North Sea was frozen, all the way across"), barely eight months after the fatal accident in which my parents lost their youngest child (a boy, Tobias, run over at the age of six by a cement-mixer as it backed over a pedestrian crossing in the nearby shopping street). My birth an event so unique and providential in the eyes of HEHH, my father and procreator, that it established a bond forever between him and the Almighty Creator, the Eternal Author and Finisher and He that Turneth the Shadow of Death into Morning. And prepared me, the new life form, for existence in a setting as oppressive as it was enthralling.

A few years later, by the time we afterthoughts (Kaj, Libby and I) had arrived to populate the Holbein world, it had already expanded into an illusionist's *mise en scène*. A fantastic hall of mirrors in which HEHH frequently spoke of how 'passionately' he loved our mother, Anna Alida, with a dedication and ardour to which none of us could 'hold a candle'.

He was quite adamant about the way he rationed out his love.

'First comes your mother, then your mother . . . then comes nothing . . . then for a long time still nothing . . . and then come all of you.'

Yet I believe he loved her in the way many men loved women in those days, and the way some still do. As a workmanlike piece of craftsmanship. As a well-made object of superior quality. I'm not sure he actually knew her or felt the need to find out who she really was. What she liked and what she didn't. What her needs, desires or interests were. And one might wonder whether she knew all that herself.

By then the walls of our house were already hung with pictures and oil paintings. Mostly HEHH's copies of the works of great artists. Manet's *Olympia*. *The Turkish Bath* by Ingres. Eugène Delacroix's *The Death of Sardanapalus* (inspired by Lord Byron's play). In that painting one sees how the king, who is about to commit suicide (I always thought it was because he was incurably ill), has all his possessions destroyed. His harem, his slaves and his horses. He himself watches indolently from a divan without raising an eyebrow. The concubine whose throat is being slit by a black slave was done over to look exactly like my mother.

We never questioned growing up amid representations of such multiform nudity that were always and never, in endless repetition, our own mother. And later, always, we ourselves, the Holbein daughters. Our faces stuck on to one and the same idealized body. What I do know is that we were accustomed early on to the eager goat's-eye glance, and did our best to deserve it.

There was, even then, no trace of Henne and Toddie. It was as though they had always been grown-ups, their childhoods a mere soap bubble. A brief play and shimmer of light, obscured from sight to the outside world and already burst and gone by the time we moved into their old room at the back of the house. They were married, had children, didn't seem to be missed. I know that my father didn't think they were very smart.

'Not enough sense to come in out of the rain' and 'as thick as two short planks' were standard comments about Henne and Toddie, comments we perhaps did not entirely endorse but that we carried with us far into adulthood.

Henne, according to my mother, had been a tight-lipped child, full of secrets. Nervous and jumpy as a rabbit. Always with some ailment that required attention. And Toddie (full lips, round eyes, curly dark hair) had been the coquette, even at an early age.

My mother was my father's second start, and he must have known there would be no third. She was lively and luscious as an ample flower, an amaryllis, sighted and uncovered by my father as something special and secret. The rose on the dung heap. A valuable piece of porcelain, with a chip out of it. Perhaps she *was* the chip. He had conquered her, carried her off, wiped the dirt off of her and placed her in the house where his first family had lived, and Hennie and Toddie came with her, and there was profusion.

*

Concerning the way my parents met, how they got to know each other and became a couple, various versions made the rounds. In each of them a role was reserved for substance and appearance, money, prestige and (the potential key to) a world of beauty and art. The most tenaciously memorable of all was the one in which my father, who worked at the time for his father-in-law's collection agency, had been sent to seize the property and effects of my mother and her first husband.

The year is 1949.

Well dressed, wearing sound but fashionable shoes and carrying a black moiré document file, Henri Elias Henrikus Holbein—having made it through the war with no major breakage to speak of—strolls to the address given him, rings the bell, and Anna Alida opens the door. Neither startled nor dismayed, she shows him into the modest living room where the toddlers who were to become my sisters are playing on the rug. She says that, as he can see for himself, there is not a great deal to seize. Her grey eyes flash. Her voice is pleasantly low and permeated with an angry reserve, and he invites her to lunch. The next-door neighbour is brought in to watch the children. The two of them go to a coffee house downtown. There, in the course of two cups of coffee, she apparently unfurled for him the canvas of her life. The absent father, the illiterate mother, her grandparents passed away (the grandmother of an illness when my mother had just turned fourteen, Grandpa during a delirium, brandishing knives at invisible demons before the pot-belly stove). The teensy-weensy house in the Utrecht neighbourhood of Ondiep (sleeping in the same bed with her mother for years, the story about the Toni Boltini Circus—'if I'd wanted to, I could have gone on tour with them') and the war (her mother, who rummaged about and begged on the same street where she, at sixteen, walked arm-in-arm with a young German Wehrmacht soldier). And, finally, the bombing raids, the wound to her leg, and the over-hasty marriage to the conman, the only person who had visited her in the hospital. ('He thinks every idea he has is worth its weight in gold.')

A drab canvas against which my mother, with her face like a Madonna, must have stood out brightly; a waxy Christmas apple (inedible, but bearing the promise of health, sweetness).

I don't know whether HEHH realized at the time the dizzying depth of the social gap that divided them. Or perhaps he realized it perfectly well. Twenty-five-year-old Anna Alida must have looked up to him, this well-groomed gentleman in his worsted coat. A man who expressed himself in nice turns of phrase, and chivalrously shoved aside the writs. Who offered, the next day, to buy shoes for her two little daughters. Observant and attentive as he was, he had seen that they walked around the house in dirty stockings . . .

I suspect that, after a couple of weeks of secrecy with my mother (covert rendezvous in hotel rooms, meals taken beneath the glow of matte-glass globes), Henri's years with his first wife sank from sight and seemed nothing more than part of a game he had been playing only to kill time until this new, more exciting life came along, with Anna Alida as chaos incarnate; a life that would let him slip the grasp of his too-tightly-strictured universe. To escape an obligation from which he longed to free himself, before the noose could draw any tighter.

Later, whenever my father spoke of the years with his first wife (which he almost never did, just as he hardly ever spoke of the children he'd had with her), he did so coolly and with amazement. As though he too could hardly believe that he had once lived with that older, waistless daughter of a rather prosperous businessman, and wasted time in his father-in-law's stately house on long, meandering man-talk—brandy and cigars. Or that there had actually been clumsy embraces in a conjugal bed of such stout and heavy wood that it could not be moved, reminiscent of nothing so much as a coffin. Until he met Anna, our lovely mother, lovely Anna.

How did my mother, Anna Alida, and her two little daughters end up with Henri in that flat, of all places, with its flimsy floors and paper-thin walls, where every step caused the lamps to shudder and knocked plaster from the ceiling? There are two accounts. In Henri's version, it was all-consuming love and passion that made them 'leap into the fray'. In the other, Anna Alida, after her husband threw her and the children out of the house, had no choice but to move in with Henri and his first wife, before the injured party set off for parts unknown. Upon which Anna Alida became the altogether less-than-willing stepmother of his first children. In the years that followed, she herself bore him six of her own. In 1951, Ninny (born two months prematurely, and mentally handicapped), then Max in 1952, in 1956 Toby and finally we three youngest: yours truly (1962), Kaj (1963) and Libby (1967).

Together the two of them started a new life which, after Henri's standing dismissal from the firm belonging to his father-in-law (who was not amused), consisted for a long, long time of a scramble to stay ahead of the direst poverty. A life in which his dream of ongoing inspiration and creative liberty (with muse at hand) crashed hard, day in and day out, against the rocky coast of a new reality.

Who, after all, in those post-war years, in that tainted era of joiners-in, of silent lookers-on and witnesses to a much more horrible reality, felt any need to root about in their own inner life? My father wanted to be an artist so badly. How badly my mother wanted to play a different role (one that mattered) in society. The Nuremberg trials had come and gone, yet Henri Elias's elder brother still conferred upon his newborn son the (middle) name of Adolf.

And six-year-old Henne, pale and spindly, and five-year-old Toddie, chubby and cheerful (wild and full of bravura, which made her seem like the eldest), chased each other around the cluttered rooms and hid beneath the beds. Stared at the tall, dignified man with clear-blue eyes who spoke French and Latin and recited entire passages from the Bible and from novels by heart. And who had bought them such shiny patent-leather shoes.

Perhaps Henri was confused by how quickly the two girls began calling him "Papa" and complying with his wishes, and in that saw corruption. Too ready a surrender, a treacherous and even despicable trust. For him, their most striking trait would have been their almost other-worldly attractiveness, which he also saw in our mother in a more detailed, earthier, riper form. As though she'd brought along two new shoots of herself. Two tulip bulbs with no other purpose than one day to blossom forth and grow to look like her. I imagine that, for a time, he was mad about them and couldn't get enough of their splendour.

The way they sat in their chairs, plate in front of them, holding a sandwich. Their bare little legs swaying back and forth beneath the table, their arms with those delicate rounding at the shoulders. The unbridled greediness with which Toddie ate, and Henne's slow, deliberate chewing of her food. How they explored their new residence: Toddie the commander, headmistress and chief, Henne reticent, alert, but always prompt to follow. It couldn't have been long before he started in on their (re)education.

More than anything, HEHH was annoyed by rowdiness, by 'foolish and senseless giggling' and sloppiness. Matters he regarded as obstructive to the minimum precondition for creative work. He was a man of the era of mastery and belief in the free state known as genius, and he did not tolerate having that chipped away at by the common, the human, the childlike and banal. The only one from whom he accepted such behaviour was Anna Alida, our mother.

By comparison, Henne and Toddie must have seemed almost unreal. Young as they were, he must have caught sight of something nebulous and protean in them. As though the contours of their lives had changed shape too early. HEHH liked to see himself as an ascetic, someone who sought the beauty and harmony in all things. For the equilibrium tucked away in formulae that were there to be deciphered, codes to be cracked.

But Henne lisped and often had a runny nose. And Toddie couldn't read her own name yet.

At first, his irritation must have surprised him too. The way his cheeks burned when they didn't understand him, didn't do or care about what he asked. When they went on making noise when he had called for silence. His white-hot flashes of rage when he wasn't taken seriously. He possessed little feeling for humour and could not stand to be mocked. Whenever he noticed even the faintest sign of something that resembled belittlement, there was a rumbling and a thundering in his psyche and we were on hand to witness the explosion. How he beat one of us rhythmically until my mother shouted: 'Stop, you're going to kill her if you don't stop!' And the grim, in our eyes almost comical 'whaddoeyecare' that was his response.

And Henne and Toddie must have looked at him questioningly, just as we would, when he raised his voice. Or expressed his displeasure in long, incomprehensible sentences. And later, they must have reacted almost before he had a chance to speak. Each in her own way. Henne in silence, her lower lip drawn in. Toddie provocatively, the fingers of her little hand spread out against her left thigh, chin held high.

Who's to say whether he, like the analyst he was in fact, kept track of his own interventions and examined their effects with interest? Whereby the hand that herded and kneaded Henne and Toddie (and, later, us) in their case cut away some superfluous thing here, drew out something else a bit more there, then pressed it all back into shape?

There is a mutable family anecdote that I've recounted often; meanwhile, more and more facets have been cut into it, like the face of a diamond, even though it is still unclear with which of us Holbeiners it actually has to do. According to Toddie, Henne was the direct object, while Henne insisted it was impetuous Toddie, and yet others in our household will claim that it was me. What strikes me only now, decades later, is how often this history in miniature was passed along by its auteur and presented to us as an edifying parable.

The piano in the snow

A dark-green balcony, swirling flakes.

A long, grey street and drifting snow.

Stubborn, in her underwear, on a frozen stage: one of the Holbein girls.

My mother at the table, wringing her hands: 'Let her in . . . let her back in, Henri.'

My father: 'One more minute, Anna. I know what you're thinking, but if I don't stay on top of this *now*, if I don't clamp down *now* . . . The whole afternoon in a fuss and all she can do is think in terms of *meum* and *tuum*.'

My father's sister Bettina had sent one of us the miniature piano: a bright-red, varnished one from the German firm of Schoenhut. Another of us, having claimed earlier to have no interest in the instrument, was soon overtaken by mordant jealousy and regret concerning that earlier decision.

The squabbling began.

Tumult, a racket, turmoil. One child hammered away at the keys, the other whined that it wanted to play too.

'Give it here, I want to, I'm allowed too!'

Clang! Clang! Clang! 'It's mine!' 'It's mine!' 'No, it's mine!'

The Schoenhut day-care-durable, thirty-seven-key (three-octave span) was promptly yanked from a pair of hands.

'Mine . . .?! Not even the air you breathe is yours.'

'It's mine . . . I got it!'

'Really? Yours? Well, shall we talk for once about what's mine? Shall we take a good, hard look at that? Let's see . . . that sweater and that skirt you're wearing . . . and those tights . . . you got them from me . . . I paid for them. And that headband, those shoes . . . take it all off.'

(Exeunt.)

Wearing only her underpants, the child stands among the garbage bags on 'the balcony' (Henne's version).

Or, naked and barefoot, outside the front door in the wet portico (Toddie's version).

It is, twice over, a wondrous sight: the girl beside the snow-powdered milk and yoghurt bottles (lined up like a Greek chorus against the railing), the girl outside by the green front door. Pale cheeks, the dark scowl, the scarlet instrument pressed against the hard stomach and belly.

Snow that swirls, snow that drifts. Not a single snow-flake is like another.

And the cineast who views all this and knows that he is framing an intense, indelible memory. A crystalline masterpiece.

'Henri, she'll catch her death . . .'

'Couldn't care less—couldn't care less.'

Or, in a more tender version: 'One more little minute won't hurt anything.'

Shortly after moving in to the draughty upstairs apartment, apparently, a listless torpor came over our mother, like a stray cat that has happened upon some place to rest its bones. In common with many male artists, HEHH liked to see her as his muse, an object to be "kept" in a modest (gilded) cage that he could turn round and round to admire and provide himself with inspiration. Which is not to say that he couldn't be courtly, sometimes even to the point of submissiveness or servility. But then, like in Sacher-Masoch's *Venus in Furs*, only as part of a theatrical, sadomasochistic game in which she "commanded" him and he "allowed himself to be commanded", without her enjoying any actual position of independence or freedom of choice. Which is, generally speaking, perhaps more commonly the case than we may hope or believe.

In the first years of their marriage, Henri would have liked to parade Anna Alida around as his prize. Her beauty, however, was of such class and polish that it caused her lack of education, refinement and background to stand out even more shrilly. Precisely because she was not stupid—she was more intelligent, quicker on the uptake and more facile in her thinking than he—my mother laid bare the core of my father's erotic longing and social bias.

In the years to come, as he grew accustomed (more quickly and easily than expected, in fact) to being addressed as "sir", to having his own private office and secretaries who knocked timidly on the door to ask if they could bother the boss for just a moment, she was expected to remain content with her life as a housewife and with the growing opportunities for shopping. After Henri's (initial) social degradation, and in synchronicity with his steady climb, the house became filled with bric-a-brac: statuettes, vases, mirrors, a silver-plated brush and comb set. A satin bath-robe for my mother. And with books: collected volumes of Mauriac, Diderot, a watercolour-illustrated edition of Baudelaire's *The Flowers of Evil*, and art books (which I later inherited in their entirety). Whenever he gave her a lecturing, she would look at him from the corner of her eye, pull tight the panels of her bottle-green peignoir, expel the smoke from her lungs and, with vitriolic glee, switch to a proletarian Utrecht dialect. That "street language" in which she revelled, and that Toddie in particular adopted from her with enthusiasm.

And so, long before my existence became a reality, there raged within our household an authentic class struggle.

There was no question of sharing. Through the house ran a path taken only by my father, and over which Henne and Toddie certainly were not allowed to move. Tradition had it that they cared nothing for books, art or classical music. They were given no books, art or music. They were supposed to earn those, but showed no interest. 'Brainless creatures, perfect imbeciles.'

They liked candy.

Poking my head up behind the transom window, I watch what happens. How he tutors the two girls at first. Civilized, respectable behaviour: knees together. Fending off their sticky, clinging kisses (their soft arms around his neck, the compactness of their upper bodies ... in the very first week!). How they caromed around the house like a pair of mandarin oranges, climbed on to his lap. Nuzzled up against him. (He could have been anyone!) How they were prepared to betray each other in the wink of an eye and to blame each other for minor infractions, encroachments on Holbein property. Fingerprints on a polished tabletop. Hair in a sink. Putting their mitty moles on his expensive brushes.

'Look, Daddy?' (A single sable hair.) 'I didn't do it . . .'

Cluster-violations of the rules with which he regulated daily life. Despite his direction and instruction, their thoughts kept meandering off to their own trivial wishes and desires. Chocolate sprinkles on their bread (preferably more than the other had). Clothes, a toy . . .

My mother always referred sniffishly to Henne and Toddie's first father as 'a ridiculous mistake'. In the memories of my sisters, too, he seemed to have left behind little more than the picture of a man with floppy ears and hair slicked straight back, gleaming with grease. Or of the faceless (for HEHH himself had scratched that face out and filled it in with ink) body in a couple of photos.

Henne, though, insisted that once, when she was very ill, he had picked her up in the middle of the night, wrapped her in a blanket and driven with her to the coast. On the beach they had looked at the moon and the sea together. The wind was blowing very hard and she'd had to throw up, but he had been very sweet to her. This, according to my mother, was nothing but a fabrication by the 'pathological liar' that Henne was from earliest childhood on. Just as the reaction from Toddie (who sometimes stuck up for her and claimed to have been with them too, but at other times denied everything) was proof of their incomprehensible jealousy and eternal rivalry.

At what point do we know who we are? And does it matter?

Not much is known about HEHH's youth, and the little that *is* known is a ragbag: a pile of splinters, the debris of legend.

He was the first son born of the second marriage of a staunch Catholic, who, in 1912, one year after the death of his first wife, wed his housekeeper, a Francophile '*dame*' who dealt in proverbs and maxims and cared sternly for

39

my father's older half-brother, the nine-year-old half-orphan from her husband's first marriage. Born in 1914, in an era that was masculine, patriarchal and dominated by the Church, my father came of age between two devastating world wars. *Grands Guignols* of violence which, in retrospect, appear so firmly bound together that at times the period between seems to me no greater than the space between the boot heels of a rampantly destructive giant. Roving the earth and stamping on all that was human in that century, which Huizinga referred to as 'the bitterest of all centuries'.

My father rarely spoke of his younger years. Once he said that not a day went by that he did not think about his parents. But what it was exactly that he thought about them, we had no idea; he did not talk about his memories. His father, a grandpapa I never knew, was one of the first car-dealers in the Netherlands and owned his own garage. After the stock-market crash in 1929 the company hit the skids and continued to careen downhill. A series of bank-ruptcies followed, which in turn set in motion a series of *hejiras*. The entire family, now consisting of five children, packed up and moved to different towns again and again, on the run from creditors.

From the scarce anecdotes, one deduces that our grand-father was a hot-tempered and fairly inconsistent man who cursed as he forbade his garage personnel to use strong language: ('If anybody does any goddamn cursing around here, then I'll do it my fucking self!'), and that our paternal grandmother, with the posh French surname Lambremont, wrote in a lovely hand.

No, this is hopeless.

Poking around like this in search of the childhood of Henri Elias Henrikus Holbein is like sticking my hand into a pond from which all life disappeared years ago. The occasional goldfish floats past belly-up, and from the murky water I extract nothing more than a few branches and rotting leaves. But when I watch Luchino Visconti's *Ludwig*, or *The White Ribbon* by Michael Haneke, or Thomas Vinterberg's *The Celebration*, it is as though the glass wall separating my father's childhood and early adulthood from my own has been shattered, and I perceive what-must-have-been as sharply as though I were there myself. In that house, with its staunch dark-wood cupboards, with its leather-bound books behind glass. One girl and four boys (their hair shorn up close at the back of the neck) are sitting ramrod-straight at a dinner table that is covered at mealtimes with a pristinely white cloth. I feel the rush of air as the damask unfurls and settles with a snap. A man in a tailored suit, with a long face and a carefully trimmed moustache (its edges stained yellow with nicotine), is sitting at the head of the table. The look in his eye is appraising, scrutinizing. He brooks no contradiction, this man here on the eve of the new 'age of masters'. The bathroom with its marble sinks smells of moss and mint, and in the milled-stone soap-holder lies a pig-bristle nailbrush. And atop all the thinking, feeling and (secretive) dealing in the household lies the veneer of sombre, dark Catholicism, in which living creatures are forbidden to see or touch themselves, and every display of affection is a sign of weakness. A world which, in the eyes of many of my generation, seems caricatural, stiff and unauthentic. The grim air of a ritualized existence. Did they ever laugh? Was there ever room, in that Jugendstil house with the two swastikas in the tiled house front, for an impulse, for a startling idea? From whom did HEHH inherit his talent for drawing, anyway? In the house of one of my father's brothers (whom we visited only once, because—with his marriage to Anna Alida—my father placed himself outside the order of things and had virtually no further contact with his family), there were also paintings on the walls. Colourful little landscapes in ochre and green, painted by this uncle who was married to a former nun and who, a few years after HEHH's death, refused to receive me because I wrote "dirty" books.

This is what I know for certain: after a few years at the major seminary in Rijsenburg, in those days one of the bastions of Dutch Catholicism, and after a number of odd jobs (shoe salesman, sales representative, ice-cream vendor) and a marriage arranged shortly after the outbreak of the Second World War by means of an advert in the personal column, the thirty-six-year-old bailiff Henri Elias

Henrikus Holbein sought refuge in the arms of Anna Alida, the woman who was to become our mother. From that moment on he began construction on his erotic universe. A cryptic edifice. His sexual phantasmagoria.

When did HEHH become the Minotaur?

Given how difficult it is to gain access to the young man my father must have been, and how easy it is to forget that his youth too must once have been a fallow field awaiting cultivation, I realize that he was every bit as much sculpted by his times, the product of the opportunities offered by society, as was Donald Trump, the tycoon/president.

It was always HEHH who busied himself with us, who saw to our table manners and gave us our after-dinner bath in a room flecked with milky light, where we paraded before him with careless ease and an absence of shame, and stuck out our slippery little feet for him to wash. In his defence: on the heels of the horrible accident that crushed the skull and the life out of our young predecessor, Toby (my father was the one who had to identify him), it was HEHH who became both father and mother to us "puppies". He cared for our bodies and seemed to appreciate their presence, while our mother seemed only vexed by our rampant needs (for food, cleaning, caressing, oxygen) and was, in her mourning for what had been taken from her, incapable of devoting herself to them.

Leaning against that bathroom door, scratchy towel in hand, the man who was our father undoubtedly must have wondered if there was not something obscene in the way we little human creatures bent over to search for the bar of soap in flocky bathwater, our pudenda revealed in full, or slid giggling and slippery as eels down each other's back. Whereby the water spattered abundantly over the bath's edge and left his feet soaking wet.

In this house, so inconspicuous from the outside, this plain brick house with a gas fire only in the front room with its bay window, the other rooms at the back and upstairs left unheated, with its outside rooftop area known as "the flat" and its two steep stairways (which in my richly embroidered dreams appear and disappear again, like something from Escher, in a fathomless blue vacuum), we came to know the Minotaur early on.

This house where HEHH, in an intricate fusion of Christianity with the deification of the human and of the Artist as creative entity—an admixture both uniquely his own and a possibility offered by the times in which he lived—became liege and lord over the knights, pawns, rooks and bishops . . . and, on occasion, the queen. This house a playing field where all things thought, desired and feared could become real.

*

Unlike my mother or my sisters, I was never excluded from the world of knowledge, art and science. On the contrary: I was invited into it. Decked out in the bridal veil of my natal narrative ("behold, there came wise men from the east to Jerusalem . . . for we have seen his star in the east . . . till it came and stood over where the young child was . . . when they saw the star, they rejoiced with exceeding great joy") as the "most desired, most deeply wanted" child, I became caught up already at an early age in a state of enthralled anticipation concerning the gifts that would be made mine in this place to which Henri Elias Henrikus Holbein betook himself at the end of each day from the outside world, fog and rain still clinging to his coat. Transforming the statistician, who involved himself with correlations on a daily basis in his nine-to-five office job, into a benefactor who brought me treasures and presents (dolls, books), into the shaman and wizard who told us, newest grafts on the Holbein family tree, bedtime stories drawn at times from daily life (the dead brother, crushed so horribly here on earth, but an angel now in heaven), at other times made up on the spot.

The Gossamer Damsel . . . transparent as a cobweb, at midnight she wandered the ramparts of the ruined castle. Who was she, where did she come from? Why did she haunt the ruins each night at twelve, holding her hands in front of her, her fingers long and thin as a spider's legs? *Wooooooooaaaahhh!*

Or, after Kaj was tucked in and we had moved to the girls' room, Old Testament tales that HEHH, perched on the edge of the bed, recounted with great feeling for drama.

Abraham the Patriarch whom the Almighty Lord told to sacrifice his own son and slaughter him like a lamb. Joseph, son of Jacob and Rachel, the favourite eleventh of twelve sons (*well there you go, I was a favourite too*). His jealous brothers didn't like him, but one day they would all bow down before him. And David and Bathsheba (first she was married to Uriah, the Hittite, but Uriah had to die because David desired Bathsheba to be his consort).

After which HEHH leant far over forward to trace a cross on my forehead with his fingernail, 'in the name of the Father, the Son and the Holy Ghost', the angels were called upon for protection, and then the ritual plop of his fountain pen, pointy pocket comb and finely curved nail scissors falling from the breast pocket of his suit jacket on to the bed, and his searching about ('Goodness, where did they get to now?') under sheet and blanket.

So I lived in a world of magic and language in which no "I" was (yet) necessary, and where the (Holbein) word was law, but at the same time the creep-through to a thicket glistening with red berries. (*Papa ... Mama ... later ... night ... be quiet. For God so loved the world that He gave His only begotten son.*) Long before the ABCs started at the

Bible school on our street, I was crawling in and out of that thicket, my scratched-up arms filled with treasures, feeling proud and rich.

In each of us, perhaps, resides a fear of what may one day be brought about in our lives, even before we recognize it—this perfectly usual base tone of our existence—as fear.

The child longs for magic, the child longs for education.

The dolls that run through the hallways in the deep of night, dance on all the beds, chairs and tables, and who, when the sun rises in the east, turn out to be atop the dresser in the parents' bedroom!

('Oh, what a rumpus, ach, what a row they made again last night, your Bella, Stella and Corrie.')

The tin cups under which an object disappears, the tip of the nose removed from the nose itself and then put back on again.

And in the morning hours, when Anna Alida is still asleep (and she's always asleep, Elsie Marley is grown so fine, she won't get up to feed the swine, but lies in bed till eight or nine, lazy Elsie Marley . . .), the soft white bread that Henri cuts into long, thin strips and smears extra-thick with butter and sprinkles with sugar.

So we must not rule out the possibility that the child, at least for the time being, raises no objection to being chosen, at some little distance from the other children occupying the Holbein household, or those visiting said household with persistent regularity, to enter that universe with its sacred runic script (and language as the golden glow-worm lighting up the cave).

I must have been about six when HEHH presented me with a fat book bound in red linen, containing the fairy tales of Hans Christian Andersen, with the irresistible and unrivalled watercolour illustrations by the Polish artist Janusz Grabiański (a name I pronounced in a whisper: Januszzzzzz ... januszzzzzz ... only later did I understand it to be an abbreviation of Januszoon).

It was my first real book. It had weight, it existed, and it was truer to life than I was, more than any of us were in the shadowy world of Holbein.

I was ill at the time, running a high fever. When I started reading 'The Nightingale' ("In China, you know, the emperor is a Chinese, and all those about him are Chinamen also . . ."), I tumbled directly into the wonder described by Nabokov in *Lectures on Literature*: "In a sense, we all are crashing to our death from the top story of our birth to the flat stones of the churchyard and wondering with an immortal Alice in Wonderland at the patterns of the passing wall. This capacity to wonder at trifles—no matter the imminent peril—these asides of the spirit, these footnotes in the volume of life are the highest forms of consciousness . . .". Glowing beneath the blankets, walking on the hand of the writer from the Danish town of Odense, I read the stories of princes and princesses. The stories of tinkers, swineherds, soldiers and little scrabbling animals. And even those of trees or plants or inanimate objects like a top. About characters who had as yet no voice, possessed no fixed shape or temporarily lost the one they had, or even surrendered it. Like little Karen, who has her feet chopped off to keep from dancing to the old lady's grave. Or the mermaid. ("The prince asked who she was and how she had got there, and the little mermaid looked at him with her deep-blue eyes, very sweetly and at the same time most sadly; she was, after all, unable to speak.") The cruel sea hag cut off her tongue and tail and gave her human legs, but every step she took felt "as though she walked on the tips of glowing needles or the edges of sharpened knives". Alas—she fell to foam on the waves before being taken up into the choir of daughters of the air, and the prince's wife she never became. The little matchstick girl died an awful death of cold. Yet however tragic the events may have been, no matter what tribulations the creatures I read about experienced, and no matter how abrupt or transitory their physical form, each time they were given a soul, a nature of their own. Anyone who acted puffed-up was brought low right away. Anyone who clung to a false, illusory view of the world was confronted with the good, the real and the true. 'I'll make your horses prance for you,' said Big Claus, and, seizing a length of wood, he struck the only horse Little Claus had on the head, and he fell dead instantly. 'Oh, now I have no horse at all,' said Little Claus, weeping. But after a while he skinned the dead horse (a practical man, still) and hung the hide to dry in the wind. Then he put the dry skin into a bag and, tossing it over his shoulder, went to a neighbouring town to sell it.

Desire, disease, starvation, death, violence, poverty, deprivation . . . scores of grisly, terrifying matters, the pure urge (and strategy needed) to survive, in Andersen it all came marching past, just as everything passed under review in our Holbein household and would go on doing so. The worlds I read about, the world I lived in, ran side by side; they mixed and mingled. It was as though I, the severely myopic daughter (a diopter of −10.00 and no glasses until I reached the age of seven), had been given my first pair of eyes, and a white-mirrored edifice rose up across from the seething, roiling darkness to which I had already grown accustomed.

On the mantelpiece in our front room, in a silvery frame, was a little photograph of our dead brother. (He was wearing shorts, a striped sweater and glasses.)

Ninny (forceps delivery, oxygen deficiency) came home and wanted to know why God had squeezed him so hard at birth, whether he would ever turn out all right, and whether one day he would be able to learn too.

(Sorry, ma'am, this one's perhaps a bit half-baked, this one's a bit off, should probably have stayed in the oven a bit longer, sir, given the dough a wee bit more time to rise . . .)

'Do you guys remember?' asks Ninny, asks Max too. *Do we ever, do we ever*, we chant. The way we used to set the table on Sundays with a white tablecloth? Yeaaaah. The way the gas fire roared in the front room? Yeaaaah. The way the chicken fat crackled and hissed in the oven, remember that too? Yes, oh yes. And how about that time, at Christmas, when the real candles (!) on the tree genteelly set the curtains afire?

Yes. Yeaaah, oh yeaaah!

Henri Elias had ripped the curtains from the rails with his bare hands and danced on them till all the sparks were extinguished!

Yes, that's right, that's what he did! Oh yeah, oh yeah!

And all was well. Really and truly. Both inside and out, at one and the same time.

And Father says that I'm the smartest, that the others (at home) can't hold a candle to my intelligence.

Did HEHH know back then how grand it was, the gift of language, letter and book with which he prepared me and kneaded me in the direction of his (physical) needs and wishes? I, in any case, had as yet no idea of the gift's impact. Just as, for a long, long time, I remained unaware of the poison, the infection at the root.

The door of the parental bedroom swings open . . . I'm six, maybe seven. There is the big linen cupboard with its mirrored door that captures the whole room, reflects and brings it to life again, but then different. The bed with the chintz spread, dotted with faded flowers. On the window-sill the porcelain Virgin in pastel hues, yellow and blue, with Anna Alida's real deep-sea-diver pearl necklace draped over it.

Going into it, truly going in . . . this impressive curiosity cabinet, just like the Royal Society of Science. To sit there as the only girl, on the creaky leather chair, and smoke the old pipe tobacco of wisdom and excellence. To shoot the titi monkeys out of the trees (like Humboldt) and study their behaviour. To drive the horses into water rife with electric eels (just like Humboldt). Separate the child from the mother. Keep a Kaspar Hauser of one's own, to teach one's own words.

Have, be, become, remain, seem, resemble, appear, be called, consider and appear a counsellor, a comrade, a Nietzschean soulmate.

'Let's talk today about the movement of the heavenly bodies, the orbits of the planets, the golden mean.' 'Never start a drawing in the middle, and don't cover the entire page.'

'Don't move your hand up and down so hard . . . gentler, gently, damn it . . .'

With a grim smile, and not without regret, I send this courtly child back down the dimly lit hall to the place where the piper piped and no knowledge came without remission, the levying of a special goods and services tax. And where, just like the others, she was the piggy.

THE NEST OF THE ARRIERA

O UR PART OF town, Lombok, was a typical working-class neighbourhood, thrown up in the early years of the twentieth century around the Royal Hamburg Lead and Zinc Rolling Mill on Utrecht's west side. The main streets were built specially for the office personnel; the factory workers were housed in the smaller cross-streets where Henne and Toddie would live later on. Straight through the centre of the neighbourhood, like a real canal, ran Kanaalstraat, and all the streets had names that fitted the neighbourhood's Indonesian theme. There were side streets named after islands and provinces (Bandoeng, Bali and Borneo Street). The architecture, particularly in East Lombok, consisted of squat workers' homes in dark, hard brick (baked at high temperatures in rotary kilns), set along streets running perpendicular to Kanaalstraat, which, like our "own" Damstraat, was possessed of more grandeur and taller homes with white facing bricks, ridge beams and recomposed granite porticos. On Kanaalstraat itself stood a bathhouse built in 1915 (at the initiative of the Association for Public Wash-houses: around the turn of the century a campaign had been launched for the advancement of public hygiene, especially for the lower classes) and on Muntkade there was the Museum of Coins and Currency, which closed its doors only in 2013. Damstraat, where we lived at number 11 bis, above a paint store and mattress dealer's (called, quite enigmatically, the Bed & Baby House), ran from the top of Leidsekade and the busy square at Westplein to the bottom of Vleutenseweg, and was named after the former manor grounds known as "Damlust". It was a real place, with co-ordinates in both space and time: DD (decimal degree) latitude 52.0910451, longitude 5.104154600000015/ DMS (degrees, minutes, seconds) latitude (N) 52°5'27.762", latitude (E) 5°6'14.956".

I looked this up recently; sometimes I seem on the verge of forgetting.

The start of our colony's lifecycle was marked by the nuptial flight of the Arriera (Anna Alida). The inseminated queen (ant) made her descent at this place somewhere around 1950, painlessly shed her gossamer wings and began exploring the territory. On a patch of soft, open soil she dug a vertical shaft, the end of which she rounded off into a little chamber. This retreat became the first element in our nest, which was destined to expand to enormous proportions, and also the spot where our mother would spend the largest portion of her fertile life.

It was probably not a very safe nest, not even at the start.

My first memories of the Queen Arriera are olfactory and rife with synaesthesia: scarves that emitted a powdery haze, nylon stockings, the vague odour of fish, a whiff of trimethylamine in a light concentration in her lap, cigarette smoke, dark (alto) voice (*Unforgettable, that's what you are*, Dinah Washington), her grey eyes that sparked on the cold and clammy, melancholy Mondays when she moved agitatedly through the maze of that nest.

There are days when these memories carry me right to the gate that seals off an area where I was not merely HEHH's child, but still belonged as well with the Queen Arriera herself and she with me, and where our heartbeats pounded out their rhythm in unison.

It was 1966, I was four years old, when the vault closed. Inside it, Anna Alida, gravely ill: pregnancy toxemia and thrombosis. She lay in the repository of the parental bed, in the top-floor bedroom, expecting what was to be her last child. Sequestered from me and my little brother Kaj, with our sticky hands, snotty noses and uncombed hair, she was accessible only through and under the watchful eye of HEHH, sentinel on the parapet. We were allowed to visit her once each day, by twilight, shortly after dinner. Glued into the picture album Anna Alida gave me the year before she died (each of us received an album like that) is a coarse-grained sheet of notebook paper. *Dear Mama, I love you very much, ma'am, and I hope that you will feel better very soon.*

I remember writing that note at the circular dinner table, HEHH standing over me, checking my spelling, and remember too that the rooms were filled with an ever-expanding, grimy darkness in which all contours faded, even those of my mother. And that she was swollen, thick ankles, thick stomach, puffed up, changed. The house sombre, and Libby, once born, a ball of lightning in its midst. ('This is your little sister, she's very small, make no noise, and you children are permitted to come look at her, wash your hands, all of you, and don't touch her . . .') A thing inexplicable and tender beyond compare. Wobbly and animated, filled with chortles and light. An air bubble of the purest pastel, my baby sister. Another memory, roiling up out of darkness, is that of Libby, plump and rounded, in the tall highchair at the table, cinched tightly into her blue-leather harness lined with snowy-white wool, pressing her little fingertips into the crustless slices of bread on the plastic dish bearing the likeness of the Little-Engine-That-Could. She would remain sitting there (while Max, Ninny, Kaj and myself left one by one for our schools and day-care centres respectively, and my father left for his office) until Anna Alida awoke and came down around ten or eleven. Usually only after Henne or Toddie rang the bell—ding-dong—or opened the front door by snagging the rope that unlatched it from the inside, then struggling up the stairs with a baby of their own in its stroller.

Both were young mothers. Their first pregnancies coincided with my mother's last. Returning home from school, I would find them chattering and smoking. Their babies in the playpen or on a rug in the back room, and Libby still in her highchair, her buttery fingers covered with chocolate sprinkles squashed to flyspecks.

Had I, at that age, seen on the silver screen the temperamental movie stars of Italian neo-realism, like Sophia Loren, I would certainly have recognized my mother and sisters in the lives they portrayed. Lives like those lived by countless other marginalized women in our seemingly staid bishopric. Like the single mothers who lived around the corner from us on Kanonstraat, in their flats without showers or laundry spaces. Or the "Monday girls" along that same street, their window displays favouring pink and white porcelain statuettes of can-can dancers or rococo kissing couples (the women with miniature fans in their ceramic hands, the men in trousers ending in a bow above the knee), who of course received company on other days of the week, but never more than on that first one after the weekend's disappointments. Early in the morning, before the shops came to life, Kaj and I would see them lined up at the baker's, unrigged and their hairdos all a-shambles, like kewpie dolls played with too roughly by naughty children.

Or the memory of brother Ninny, our Holbein house-hold- and garden-variety idiot, seated on his wooden chair in the hallway, hidden beneath the jackets on the coatrack with a transistor radio on his lap, listening to the Beatles. I remember him doing that when I was a toddler. Serene as the 120-year-old Úrsula Iguarán in Márquez's *One Hundred Years of Solitude*. Only recently have I started to wonder how he ended up in that vale of shades, beneath that rind-pile of heaping skins and hides reeking of humankind. Was it a refuge he sought out for himself? Or was he (the only one of us to visit Henne on her last birthday and who—water-bearer, man of sorrows—still weeps loudly whenever he speaks her name) banished there by my father, who after all tolerated no fools and wished to be surrounded solely by the neat and the unwavering? Or by my mother, driven mad with irritation? But I digress. The (childhood) story of Sophia Loren and that of my mother exhibited, in any event, a number of striking parallels.

Like Loren, my mother grew up fatherless (and bereft) in surroundings where she was looked down upon, and in a Europe lacerated by war. Like Loren, she grew from a skinny, painfully shy girl into a striking beauty, and like Loren she took refuge with an older man.

In the year I was born, Sophia Loren, who seemed the personal embodiment of post-war reconstruction, was already a star (with an Oscar under her belt for her role as the mother in *Two Women*). All on her own she seemed to have become the age incarnate, the personification of all those women who had suffered under hard-line regimes in our turbulent Europe.

Yes, my mother and sisters all resembled Sophia, and at the same time they didn't. They resembled, in fact, all the roles Sophia had played and would go on to play, like Antonietta in *A Special Day*. And there was something in the way they smoked, laughed, talked, groused and sat together that made them seem strong and weak at the same time. There was no way I could know what made this so, and back then I did not know. They were remote, and at the same time right there. A glorious something I couldn't understand. Even though there was also an element in those get-togethers that instilled dread in me; something oppressive about the smoke spiralling through the rooms, the ash-caterpillars tipped from cigarettes or falling untapped because they'd grown so long, much too long. And Anna Alida's indifference and the absence in her of any feeling other than rancour, irritation or bare-faced disgust with soft, living things. Like the cat, Jojo, when it rubbed purringly over her ankles, 'oh, yuck, god no, go away,' and which expanded and settled over us. Abhorrence for our 'gooey hands', our voices and recurring presence. Oh, are you back again already, she would say when school was out, even when we had been gone all day and eaten lunch at Henne's, are you back already? Even Libby, cute as a bunny rabbit, gave her no pleasure.

Anna Alida had just turned forty. In those late 1960s, a strident whistle was sounding for women in general, housewives in particular, to signal that the best days of their lives were done and gone.

Back to Loren. With her full-blown sexuality and a beauty bounteous as it was earthy, she made you feel that out of all that poverty, war and want, something gorgeous could still grow. So that in the roles she played, and beyond that too, she became the great symbol of all those lives in which the focal point, more than any political choice for one side or the other, had been the pure will to survive. It was, after all, during those war years in particular that such great demands had been placed on women: house-wives, factory workers, secretaries, nurses, mothers, work-ing women. Fighters, biters and teeth-clenchers with smouldering passions and desires of their own. Charged with the maintenance and safeguarding of Normal Life, under anything-but-normal conditions.

Within the four walls of home there may have been a heavy rumbling, a sputtering, quaking, simmer, burble and boil ... ('Lie still, or I'll break your neck,' a voice whispers in deepest darkness), but outside those walls these guardians of the precept of the tidy, unviolated house shook the dust from their feet and walked on, shoulders back, chin up. Set course for the ideal of the clean, safe and orderly life, something yours truly scoffed at often enough. Or set course towards, at least, a life in which one's good name and honour were not further besmirched by some imbecile out waving the family's dirty laundry on the village square. (Whereby, to make matters easier, one ignores the question of who actually soiled that laundry so badly, or squashed it all into one big clump at the bottom of the basket.)

1968, '69, '70. Morning. There goes Anna Alida; the weekend is over, you can hear the anger and resentment in the way she lugs the vacuum cleaner, ram-bam-slam, around the top floor like an armadillo on a leash, banging across every threshold and against all the baseboards. From the boys' room where Ninny and Kaj sleep in their metal bunk bed, past Max's cork-lined alcove (once a storage space), and into our room, the one I share with Libby. In the loud irritation with which she cleans Libby's baby bed and pulls the flannel sheet and wetted blue mattress-protector out from under me, empties the chamber pot of wobbly turds and flocky strings of seed (Henri's spawn).

'It's Monday. Everybody out. And who gets to clean up after all you lot? Who's stuck with the mess, the whole dirty, filthy, stinking business?' 'What's wrong with you now? My god in heaven, another bellyache? Bellyache, bellyache. Faking it to get out of school, isn't it? If you only knew how rotten *I* feel!'

To be honest, as I should be, I have few memories of my mother as a warm, welcome spot. True, her helplessness and impotent rage at (what she saw as) her imprisonment often, especially when I was a bit older, made me feel like screaming: 'So do it, leave, why don't you!?', yet there is another, second reality to which I must admit. In exchange for her bottled rage, she was granted (minor) privileges and accepted them, embraced them.

If I have till now paid more attention to the shiny, nigh-inaccessible world of HEHH (for it was that which fascinated me, and certainly not the drab, dust-ball-piss-pot world of Anna Alida), it is because of how easily we forget or censure that which is nearby but has no glamour or status.

Towards the end of her life, in memories that bubbled to the surface like marsh gas, my mother spoke of her own humiliations. Of the smirch of having no father, and the harsh poverty and disdain that accompanied that, the perpetual, odious grin of her mother's dentures in their glass of water atop the nightstand, like Yorick's mocking sneer ("here hung those lips that I have kissed"). And how my father, in their early days, had been unable to choose between "his" two wives. Grandpa Holbein had actually felt compelled to come by one day, to impose order on the chaos. Slamming his cane down on the floor until it broke, he'd shouted grimly: 'Enough's enough! Who's it going to be, this one or the other one?'

'When I was little, I had nothing,' my mother said. 'I played butcher's shop with sugar animals that had gone all hard, 'moooo', chop off its head, 'moooo', chop off its head, or school, and the pupils were buttons.' Yearningly, she leafed through my schoolbooks. 'If I'd been born these days, I'd know what to do. I'd have been gone a long time ago . . .'

In the early 1970s, Lombok underwent a drastic facelift. With the construction of the Hoog Catharijne complex and its blinking array of retail stores, Kanaalstraat—the sparkle-packed shopping street of yore where Libby and I had stared greedily from the bay window at the display of the De Poort toy store across the street—became the down-at-heel main street of a neighbourhood in decay. In the 1980s and around the turn of the millennium, as urban renewal was rolled out in all major cities in the Netherlands, our neighbourhood too got its turn to be tackled and done up.

In the front room, HEHH stands at the bay window, he clears his throat and files his nails.

He was a gentleman, we considered him a gentleman, and our mother, Anna Alida, mostly crude and common . . .

Even today, a part of me stands in awe of the smooth inscrutability, the metallic gleam or restrained streamlining of objects and utensils that in my mind go along with the work and garb of a "perfect gentleman". The scrupulously tailored inside pocket of a blazer. A paisley necktie made of silk. The stylized eroticism of men's suits (crispy-clean white shirts and cufflinks of precious metal with stripes), in the bathroom shaving soap, alum, brand name "De Vergulde Hand", on the edge of the white porcelain sink), the whole props cabinet of white-collar masculinity so thoroughly explored in books and movies like *Bright Lights, Big City*, *American Psycho*, *Glengarry Glen Ross*, *Wall Street*, *The Wolf of Wall Street* and *Shame*.

I am nine years old and I'm standing beside my father's steel desk in the office on Varkenmarkt, deeply under the spell of these things; like a believer in the presence of one of Moses' knucklebones, bits of straw from the Holy Manger or a few strands of hair from the head of the Blessed Virgin. The Success planner in its cognac-coloured leather cover, the deep-blue Parker fountain pen, the stack of spotless white typing paper in A4 format, not a dog ear or raffle in the pile. The tall, narrow filing cabinet with its tiny key . . . even the silvery-grey dust cover on the type-writer; everything here speaks of order, control, command.

It is the summer of 1972, and far away from fickle Anna Alida and her threats ('One of these days I'm going to put an end to it, I'll jump out of the window, you just wait, you just wait, you just wait! And good luck to all of you, dealing with this whole goddam mess on your own.') I type the first little stories of my own on the Remington Rex, availing myself of long-defunct accessories like carbon paper and Tipp-Ex. While Miss Nijssen, an unmarried lady who worked at the university and had quite some clout at the Centre for Data Analysis, watched over the men's "nomadic sexual energy".

I don't know whether 1972 was the same year that my father's eye fell on the secretary. Somewhere in the family archives (cardboard boxes moved these days with increasing frequency between the attics at Max's, Kaj's, Libby's and my own home) is a photograph of a young woman, her gold-blonde hair pinned up loosely at the back. She is sitting on his desk, wearing a speckled, azure-blue dress and nylon stockings, and she could not have been much older than Henne or Toddie, no more than twenty-five or -six, this cross between Peggy Olson and the red-haired bombshell Joan from the TV series *Mad Men*.

Around the house, jokes were made about the high, arid plateau where women like my mother Anna Alida— once pretty and fecund, now robbed of anything like reason, perspective and humour—would soon be herded together, waiting only for the circling vultures to alight and pick out their dead eyes, tear out their foolish tongues.

My mother feared and hated menopause, which was presented to her as the narrow, tedious and drawn-out cordon in space and time that arrived just before something even more hideous: immolation atop her husband's funeral pyre, or abandonment in a dark wood void of human or animal sounds.

There were arguments in those days.

HEHH: 'Just stop it, shut that ugly gob of yours for once, would you, *Aleid*!' (My mother hated being called Aleid.) 'Don't forget, you used to be pretty hot to trot yourself.' And the way he said this made it clear that he was talking about everything that was vulgar about my mother, and I was ashamed of the "trotting" for which she had once been hot and not anymore, and found her vulgar as well.

We were all part of a scheme in which we played a role (or in which we and that role were one), in accordance with strict commandments and precepts. Even if those rules were written nowhere, they were as much in evidence as the laws dictated in clay in the Codex of Ur-Nammu, or Hammurabi's Code on its basalt pillar. And they were every bit as exacting and monolithic (and sometimes monstrous) too, as though they belonged to the world's first and primal laws. (Woman, thou shalt be desired, but shall not desire. Woman, when your womb grows barren and decay begins, thou shalt enter the shadows allotted you without clamour or protest.)

Oh, but what if all you have known and seen of love, tenderness and solicitude has come to life in this same place (and oh so powerfully!) for the very first time?

Libby's gentle, snuffly breathing ... Kaj in his bed, encircled by dozens of stuffed animals and teddy bears ... *If you go down to the woods today, you'd better go in disguise.* This house as a whole, in which the powerful wizard's world was hidden away. Outside it the shops, the baker's with the little sugar babies in marzipan cradles beneath crisp marzipan blankets, and the powdered custard buns, and my teeth sinking into the light-brown roll and coming to rest in the creamy layer of vanilla, the butcher with the half-cloven carcasses on hooks, Raké's textile shop and the shop that was called Raké's too but sold candy, the bike store, the hardware store, fishmonger Vos, which was also an Indonesian *toko*, with cumin-seed, ginger and rock-hard, ready-to-fry prawn crackers, where chromy fish lay side by side in trays beneath a glass counter-top thick as a man's fist, the sounds of cars, vans and buses, the quivering copper chandeliers like congealed squid adrift on the ceiling, the paintings on the walls, the little tropical birds in their cage (zebra finches, goldfinches, strawberry finches, orange-breasted waxbills, two Bengalese finches, a canary), and the furniture at home: the leatherette sofa with bluish-green cushions in plaid, the low teak-wood coffee table and the standing ashtray—a beige enamelled bowl with floral pattern and a spinning lid, where every member of the Holbein family tossed their ashes (except for us, of course, the three youngest, the nippers, the small fry), and inside of which a djinn consumed the endless supply of butt-ends. Then on Mondays (blue, chilly days, the bellowing vacuum cleaner inside the house, the bellow of the garbage trucks outside), the boiling water poured on the ashes, a deafening stench, and the killing fields of cigarette butts floating like greyish-brown maggots in a muddy-brown pond of tobacco.

And around the seance table, Anna Alida and her daughters, Henne and Toddie, great divas of misfortune and hope.

Forever and for always, for always and forever . . . times of surfeit, of deafening silence and denial. Look here, the knee-prints of our predecessors on the coconut mat, here on the landing at the foot of the stairs stood a child naked and banished, a red toy piano clutched to her bony breast, here HEHH's sons (his firstborns, to whom in this tale we pay as little heed as we do to our esteemed but promptly forsaken family friend, Sebastiaan) dug and clawed through the trash bins in search of lukewarm gravy rolls or a deep-sixed half-loaf of Lubro (the factory bread that grew stale and inedible with such amazing speed), here the wall against which one of them bashed his head by accident. Here too were sung the praises of the female genitalia, the velvety, deep spelunk of the hungry cunt, the piggy bank, the front bum, and Libby and I were the Dirty Little Fannies ('girl, come here with that dirty little fanny . . . stop being so difficult, don't be such a whiner . . . I'm your father'). Here dripping candles danced and burned on the bent boughs of a majestic Christmas tree, here Russian choruses sang the 'Stabat Mater', here the unsurpassed master HEHH took up the paring knife like thousands of other fathers, to carve the heights of us, his plentiful offspring, into the flaky doorpost. Here we were burgeoning, growing, ripening, breathless progeny, admirers and bed-wetters, here our bedroom doors had locks, an iron catch on the jamb, here mice rustled; after they had fallen still, we would find their skeletons behind a heating pipe, between the metal elements of a toaster; squeeze them too hard and you were left holding nothing but powdery grit.

Here too, once, now singularly unreachable, the warmth of a mother's lap.

And around the table, the women.

'My split's all itchy, my kittie, my cooch,' says Toddie.

'Ga-uhhhrh-agrgggh,' Henri rasps.

'God almighty, try not to be so crude for once, all right,' Anna Alida says. She takes a slug of her coffee, a drag of her cigarette.

'I don't have that, I'm not like that at all, really,' tingle-tangles Henne. 'I prefer to keep myself neat and clean . . .'

And yours truly, legs folded beneath her in the plaid-upholstered armchair, pretends to be reading—and listens. Maybe someday she'll actually understand.

How to unravel the make-up of one's existence, plumb the genome of one's own brain? Still unaware of what will one day become unbearable memory: not of the mouth that learns to close indiscriminately around all that is proffered it; an ice-cream wafer from the corner candy store, a sugary jawbreaker magically changing colours, or around the Holbein penis (with astonishing verve and truly "natural" talent, if we may say so ourselves). No, not of that, but of the triumph, over our dead brother and Anna Alida. And the steady, powerful yet lopsided development of one's powers of observation. Concerning, for example, the (blueish-grey) cycloplegic eye of the priapus in its sheath of light-blue textile, with the external collop (bag) found in male, non-testiconda mammals, of which *The Concise Grey's Anatomy* says: "the thin, brownish or brownish-pink skin contains more pigment than that of surrounding areas and has many sebaceous (oil-producing) glands and sweat glands, as well as thinly distributed, curled hairs."

What I remember is a rubberish solidity and, with some regularity, a peculiar and striking alteration known in the material sciences as phase transition, phase change or phase transformation, in response to minimal variations in pressure and temperature.

In my mouth the starchy taste of glue.

The story you appear in yourself always seems the truest one. And at the same time it is, in your eyes, the one that least resembles an actual story.

Were someone ever to ask me what I'm on about, what I'm trying to figure out with all my obsessive scribbling in Moleskin notebooks . . . with my blue BIC pen and the ink of the octopus flowing on to beige or urine-coloured pages rife with wood fibre (never the whitest white, for then the breathing halts, the words catch, the pen remains suspended in air) . . . what it is I'm trying to say with my asides in the margins (scratching away maniacally like David Bowie's Lazarus in *Blackstar*, on and on and on, across the book, over the edges, across the tabletop and down the legs), why I bedeck cupboards and doors with insects, creatures retractable and telescopic, meat-eating plants, and why I clip Ernst Haeckel's *Art Forms in Nature* from HEHH's old art books . . . ask me, in short, what it is I'm trying to get at with this narrative of which I am a part, then I'll tell them: this is an ongoing study into "home", what that means and to whom. What that is, was and one day might be. And then I'll add that I need to depict and summon up *my* house, its pathology, in lots and lots of stories and in (rhythmic, ritual) reiterations, like fractals. As the puzzle it actually was, a labyrinth, the dark side of the moon.

Anna Alida: 'It won't be long now; you people won't be seeing me around here any more. If it was up to me, I'd leave today, leave the whole shooting match for good.'

HEHH: 'You old cow, where would you go then?!'

No, I don't believe we Holbeins were ever an ordinary family. But then again, I believe we weren't particularly extraordinary either. There was chaos and confusion; a certain havoc and disarray surrounding us and our life stories, a disunity in who we were.

When I invited my mother Anna Alida to my apartment one day (I was a grown-up by then, with a daughter of my own), to confront her with my suspicions and tentative findings concerning the source of my (not altogether uninteresting, but at the same time quite overwhelming) nightmares (horrific: creatures with pincers for limbs, a sheep with glistening teeth, endless stairways, raw meat on the steps): to wit, our former life with the Minotaur, she collapsed in tears.

She sank down on to the floor in front of the meter cupboard (inside it was a bag of forgotten potatoes, with runners that scared me), we both sat on the floor, and she crawled down the hall on hands and knees, sideways, like a crab. In her floral dress, beige stockings, her heeled pumps.

So tell me. What's a girl to do?

That was the last time Anna Alida ever visited me. She never came again after that, she said she couldn't find my apartment, that she could never remember which of the four high-rise buildings it was in. By that time, the bridge between us had turned to slippery ice. At fixed times, I allowed her to be around my daughter, with whom she went for *poffertjes*, silver-dollar pancakes, at Victor Consael's, back when that legendary pancake pavilion was still open in downtown Utrecht. Or to the puppet show in Nieuwegein, where Punch and Judy chased each other around a folding theatre of chipboard and cardboard. And I would arrive at the agreed time to retrieve my daughter, at the heart of the shopping mall, and we would exchange cordialities at the handover. 'It was very nice,' she would say, 'we had lovely *poffertjes.*'

These days, I tell almost no one that I loved my mother. I'm always afraid it will sound too sentimental, or that I'll simulate an emotion or repeat one that once was real (and that then, like the emperor in the fairy tale about the Chinese nightingale, I will settle for a shiny facsimile, a copy of the real and true). Sometimes I experience that love all over again, when I see cows huddled together in a field or come across a certain derelict woman in the shopping street close to where Oleg and I live. A woman of about seventy whose face bears absolutely no resemblance to Anna Alida's. Her features coarse and hard, devoid of all beauty, nothing ladylike about them, with her long, brown cable sweater and short, greyish-white hair, yellow at the tips. She stinks like hell and waddles like a duck as she pushes her little cart out in front of her, one of those canvas pushcarts in Scottish plaid, stuffed from top to bottom with clinking bottles, and she *always* smiles when she sees me . . . then the notion that she's my mother is so powerful that my eyes smart and start watering whenever I walk by her, yes, there she goes, my mum, me old lady, my mommy—and she's homeless.

THE MINOTAUR

THERE ARE FIVE pictures of Henri from before he became the Minotaur. In the oldest of them, he's an infant on a furry rug. The next one shows him as a little boy in a classroom. In the remaining three, in which he must be seventeen, eighteen and nineteen respectively, he is always standing in the midst of a large group of young men, fellow students, in front of some kind of school: the major seminary, or, perhaps even before that, the gymnasium, the preparatory school in Nijmegen. The photos were taken on sunny days, with truncated shadow and bright light in which the building's bricks stand out one by one. My father, Henri, is tall, slender and looks a little lost. His light-brown hair (what a surprise to see that he once had a head of hair) still sweeps full and heavy across his forehead, and he is looking into the camera with a feeble smile that may not be a smile at all. The pictures are in black and white, but his pale eyes strike you right away. In one of them he is holding a cloth; they have just finished doing the dishes. On a table in front of him are a number of white cups turned upside down. In a big zinc tub are bottles. He looks neat, young and fresh in these photos (which don't include a single woman). He is wearing a white shirt, a necktie and, in the picture with the dishes, even a coat. Yes, everything is so clean . . . the gleaming cups, the students' faces, the rinsed bottles . . .

Melancholy, mourning, a sense of loss, none of that comes close to describing the effect these photos have on me. These are the early 1930s, there is still so much that has to happen. But that which is yet to happen is precipitating in time already, leaving layer upon layer there, the way powdered seashells and the skeletons of fish form mountains of limestone with snow at their summits.

On 7th January 1933, while eighteen-year-old Henri stands there with his wan smile and that white dishrag in his hands, the first issue of the NSB weekly *Volk en Vaderland* ("People and Fatherland") appears. Before the month is over, President Hindenburg will appoint Hitler Chancellor of Germany. On 20th July, the Vatican will put its signature to the concordat between the Holy See and Nazi Germany. In that same year, Dachau becomes the first concentration camp ready to receive political prisoners.

It's as though these photos play a melody for me. The siren song of an impending future (one which will harken back to an aristocratic, antique past, and raise that as its totem). The hum of someone singing with their mouth closed, from behind gritted teeth. That song is shocking, insistent, one might even call it sublime. It tells a wordless tale of wars and love and bodies that become entangled. Of chandeliers, tapers and prime numbers. Of earth, fire and wind and what it is that fire consumes: people of ash forced to live in ash houses. Of things yet to be invented and fantasies to be brought to life. It is as though I am seeing the members of an orchestra, gathered for the opening notes of an awesome symphony. And among them, one member in lone confinement, and also—in thin, sharp lines of 9H pencil (lots of clay, little graphite)—the plans for his own, modest labyrinth. Complete with the dust that will settle, the sand on the floor and the books that will be read and written . . .

And Henne and Toddie, who will one day be the first to enter it, suspecting nothing.

I don't believe I will ever find out exactly when HEHH's little visits to Henne and Toddie began. The two of them must have been very young. Our memory reaches far into the past, but what it brings us comes (I know now) more in eruptions of odours, colours and images than in language or any coherent narrative.

I doubt they were surprised to find there was a Minotaur. They must have known quite early on, in any case, that he was lingering somewhere in their vicinity; an itinerant God, as it were, who gave them (sometimes in remarkably consoling fashion) everything fatherly they would ever know in their lives.

"Harvest month is the last before winter, gore-month the first month of winter, then comes the frost-month, then the ram's month, which is the dry month, then follows the snow-month and after that the month of declining winter. Then follows the cuckoo's month, which is sowing time, then egg-tide or weaning-tide, then hay-making month, and the reaping month." Just like in the *Edda*, our house was marked by long winters.

HEHH (face red as a brick, visible row of small, white lower incisors) deposits his seed in the mouth of an eight-year-old and the rest in a hankie.

HEHH (face red as a brick, visible row of small, white lower incisors) deposits his seed in the mouth of a ten-year-old and the rest in a hankie.

HEHH (face red as a brick, visible row of small, white lower incisors) deposits his seed in the mouth of a twelve-year-old and the rest in a hankie.

Anna Alida: 'What are you two doing up there all the time? What is it with that child?'

HEHH: 'Goddammit, Aleid, get off my back, would you . . . I'm just teaching her to draw.'

(Yes, Mother, what business is it of yours?!)

Men's handkerchiefs of 100 per cent cotton in white or light-blue woven, forty by forty centimetres, with steel-grey or indigo stripes and narrow hem . . . who knows them or uses them still? Nonetheless, they can teach us a great deal. The Romans, for example, used such cloths (with names like *orarium, sudarium, focale* and *amictus*), the poet Gaius Catullus speaks of them in his texts (without mentioning what they were used for). Concerning *orarium*, one finds the following: napkin, handkerchief (*Vetus Latina*), also an article of clothing worn by a deacon in the Eastern Orthodox Church. Of the *sudarium* (sweat-cloth or *manipulus*) we know that it was a cloth of fine quality used to wipe away transpiration (and sometimes to protect the bearer from infectious diseases) or a decorative cloth carried elegantly in one hand by people of status. In particular, *sudarium* refers to two major Christian relics: the Sudarium of Oviedo (kept in the cathedral at Oviedo in northern Spain), a cloth measuring eighty-four by fifty-three centimetres and allegedly used to cover Christ's face after his crucifixion, bearing no image, only stains (although more can be seen through a microscope), and also the *sudarium* of Veronica. Tradition has it that when Veronica saw Jesus on his way to Calvary, she was so overcome with compassion that she offered him this cloth to wipe the blood and sweat from his forehead, with which his likeness was miraculously imprinted upon it. Also known as "the Veil of Veronica", it is now kept inside the statue of that same saint in the basilica of St Peter's in Rome—although churches at Milan and Jaén claim to have it as well.

But the sudarium I knew, first and foremost, belonged to HEHH.

I knew it when it was clean, I knew it once it had been used.

Unable as I was at the time to establish a link between the various manifestations of Henri Elias Henrikus Holbein, even today I must do my best to comprehend that these all lead back to one and the same creature. At such times it seems to me almost impossible, as though there has been some mistake.

It was, I must admit, and not without a certain awe, often planned to a tee. HEHH must have carried out a great many trial runs with my predecessors Henne and Toddie, and from them gained considerable insight into what prompts young children to comply. What draws them in, or at least does not frighten them off, and how their powers of perception can be moulded or influenced.

Besides which, there was a huge difference in the way reality was perceived by yours truly at four, five, six, seven, eight, nine, ten, eleven and twelve years of age. While each of those ages came with its own way of seeing things, the Minotaur also moved back and forth between, confident and bold. In our Damstraat house there was a sharp divide as well, separating life by day and life by night, with nothing in between. What took place by day preserved its contours, the colours remained clear and bright. Said colours never blended with those of the living room or kitchen, however, while some of them had a touch of coolness reserved for the lonely spaces where Anna Alida was not. The sunroom, where Henri dressed Libby and me, pulling on and off our (under)pants and pressing his nose and mouth hard against our mounds and labia to 'blow bubbles', impatient and testy if we didn't stand nice and still. Or the bathroom where, with no ado, he used his fingers with their perfectly manicured, oval nails to fiddle the worms (to which we were prone) from our anuses, and in the event of constipation (another recurring condition) applied the showerhead to give the hardened turds 'a little push' (whereby it could easily happen that the tight tunnel in which they found themselves was penetrated by his sharp index finger). In the hallway or on the stairs as well, there were hard, sudden bites to the throat or the rough pinching of the tendons in our neck . . .

But all these paled in comparison with those other, indescribable (unspeakable), awe-inspiringly "sacral" moments which took place in a murky, close "darkness" devoid of all humanity, in a space we will enter—*Bitte noch ein wenig Geduld*—soon enough.

There were, by the way, other days that simply crept along with nothing of note. Torpid Wednesday afternoons. My mother Anna Alida asleep on the couch. Henri Elias at the office, Henne and Toddie at their homes, Kaj playing at a friend's house, Libby at a playmate's on Kanonstraat (little as she was, she already pattered over there all on her own), where the girl's mother would bathe her in the zinc tub and send her home later, all powdered and loudly perfumed and with ribbons and bows in her newly pipe-curled hair. Yours truly sitting silently at the dinner table, doing my best to draw a real forest with fibrous felt-tips on a coarse, pulpy notepad. One of those evergreen ones with pine trees and firs. But I never succeeded in captur-ing in felt-tip the mystery and deep encompassment of a real forest, and snow was a recurring problem too. How could it be (this was something I truly agonized over) that I could make things darker, but not lighter? My mother was snoring lightly, ghgrhhhrr-grhhhggg, lying on the couch in her pantyhose, the soles of her stockings grey with dust and still speckled with birdseed. When HEHH came home at last there was an upsurge, expectancy, joy, and right away again a feeling of my own importance. For though my mother could get awfully irritated with me ('Go outside and play for once, would you! I'm sick and tired of you lazing about, what are all the other children shouting at you the whole time?') or ignore me completely, my father never did. At least, not until much later.

Which is why it took so horribly long before I dared to open the heavy door to that darkest of rooms. A place where, like in a sombre church or cathedral on a hill, nothing could ever have existed but the profoundest awe and a deep knowledge of the nearness of God, or in any case of an entity in direct contact with the exalted (and the abased).

Well, reader, the time has come for me to go in . . . behold the boundless kingdom of which I once was a part.

*

KATIQIWA Ka-tee-key-wah—(noun). Designation for a universe that arose from a powerful detonation in the restless mind of M.M. Holbein—around 1966 or '67. Most probably already known in 1950 or '51 to Toddiewoddie and/or Henne Fire under the name *Kracktiqiwa* or *Kuntiqiwa*.

Were I to have all the skin, flesh, blood, bones and sinew, all the metals and tools, all the felt-tip pens and accoutrements or all the languages of the world at my disposal, even if I were a master in every field, I believe I would still be unable to produce an image of the Minotaur and his labyrinth. Firstly, because the Minotaur countenanced (or had) no likeness; he showed himself only in the dark. Secondly, because sight was the superfluous, useless sense not deployed during the encounter. With the senses, in any case, something odd and inexplicable took place: they became immeshed and entangled. Eye and ear, nose and mouth, inside and outside, room and body, up and down, the numbers 1 and 2 . . .

Sometimes in this blackness there appeared the little white circle of Libby's face, pale and with open mouth, which was black as well; the nightie she wore had an embroidered yoke . . . Or suddenly a lamb loomed up (a sticker on the linen cupboard), or for a second an orange, teardrop-shaped flash of light. But none of those momentary images or flashes, which seemed to whisper that elements of the former life were perhaps still present in this space, none of those brief flickerings and perceptions of mine (which may have existed nowhere but on the inside of my eyelids) had anything whatsoever to do with or any say whatsoever in who I was, who we, the Minotaur and I, were at moments that, stretching out across centuries in this Katiqiwa, seem not to have taken place in people-time and people-space.

How can I grant you access to this labyrinth where we Holbein girls lived in succession, or ask you to come in when I myself hesitated for so long and needed (if the truth be known) Henne's pitch-keel-and-fall to do so? And where am I supposed to start my account of that habitation? With the walls through which the Minotaur evaporated at the speed of light, even though he himself was anti-light? Or with the rug like an altar cloth, marked with the smell of our poo and pee? With the hanging lamp that lit our little girls' room briefly before sleep? On its linen shade a whistling Pinocchio being followed (or following) the magnificent goldfish Cleo, ultra-orange, swimming as much as she flew, and stalking along behind her the tomcat Figaro, black as night on velvet paws. See here, here is where they were brought to bed, tucked in and kissed goodnight (tick go the nail scissors, tick the comb, plop goes the fountain pen) only to be awakened, long past the midnight hour (the bolt that sealed the room hermetically now opening with a click), and, sleep-addled, heavy, put on the pot . . . (smell of Nivea, smell of Tabac Original, smell of urine, sometimes a turd splashing ploink! into the wetness, spatters over the edge, the flowered decal on the raised front of the pot, the plastic clinging to warm buttocks . . .). And Henri vanished and dissolved, and somewhere in the impenetrable pitch: a chilly draft of air, a wee, thin strip of light that vanished and dissolved as well, and enter the Minotaur. Or maybe not enter, but emerge from the palpable, cuttable darkness packed so tightly with atoms and molecules that the Minotaur's matter could only have arisen from within that enormous pressure, a pressure which, being too much, he had to impart in turn to other matter as well.

See, and here the room which was nary a room at all, at all. A space tight and impermeable as a vital organ, with cells so abundant, moist and palpable that language was pathetic and useless there. Where no books existed and the Minotaur reigned, solemn, wise, in total desolation. Where he was on and behind the walls and rushed out over the floor like water . . . where his fingers spread across the walls and he forced his way into everything that was. Was breath, birth and life, as well as death. To transmute only in the morning hours into Henri Elias Henrikus Holbein, barely recognizable for all his clandestine, nocturnal splendour.

What can I say about the awe that accompanied life there, in that space where the wallpaper stirred, where it shook with little sighs, moans and puffs? Horror and heaviness, the complete hush, woollen strands from the carpet against the lips, while the Minotaur clipped one into billions of little black slices, in each snippet of confetti a second of eternity, which one looked at for a moment, robbed of all true senses, the gaze rolled inward: wondrous, wondrous . . .

Or that Escherian rabbit hole where frantic cells sought union and disunion . . . *dendrites, neurons, follicles, atoms* . . . where an alphabet old as the ages was recited at a whisper . . . *feeler, feeler, thorax of beetle, feeler* . . . and our bodies were united with the Minotaur . . . pressed together and pulled apart during the star-twinkle dance of nerve cells into red and green filaments, through which our blood-juice flowed, thick and slow like sap in a tree: the green blood. Or about something for which no tongue exists. Not by any fault of the Minotaur's tuition, but because of those moments when the breathing takes over. When the poor penis that is the sex organ of the male hominid forces its way so deeply into the sections that it is recognized there and, one night, even welcomed . . . push, pressing, blood-heavy black . . . blood-rennet of stink-black in the heavy sinking abdomen . . .

Here all sounds and odours come from the inside, one *is* the thumpa-thump of one's own guts, the pressure of gigantic weight until one becomes a dense planet, all elements compressed into one. One *is* the imploding universe and comes into existence even as one is destroyed. No longer human; an animal, a molecule . . . chaos, wed to the grandmaster of chaos . . . and enamoured, so deeply enamoured that in this smithy one is smelt-blasted into oneself and melted into a giant Alice.

To rise again in the morning in the guise of a kinder-gartner, and to be bundled up and dressed as a kinder-gartner (in a pair of red tights, for example, black-patent Oxfords and a plaid kilt with a pin) by the renowned HEHH, and to go to the snooty school where one is taught to make flowers with paper and scissors and punch out the shape of a donkey on a felt mat. And at Eastertide to sing the "Hosanna" with the elderly kindergarten teacher Miss Van Veen, *Van Veen, Van Veen, with her rickety old cane* . . . and weep along with her ardently at the life and suffering of our dear, *dear Lord*, Jesus Christ.

Do you see what made me hesitant?

Aeons I spent in this Katiqiwa, and I was forward and unflinching, I dared a great deal. Sometimes, yes, sometimes I long deeply for the days when I was still equal to any occasion. When blood and bones rang like a bell (*I* had outlived my brother, it was *his* skull that was crushed, *not* mine!) and every awakening was yet another triumph.

Humiliated, I hear you say? Idiots! I was not humiliated; I was raised on high as radiant-hot sun queen! To all those who would disparage the position to which I was elevated, I cry: 'Slander!' Your childhood world was miserable and beggarly, mine was grandiose! I was the one who slung the planets from their orbits with a wave of the hand, and it was in my inside-innermost innards that the powerful god who served me most humbly spilt his seed. Me, "the minion" (as I'm still wont to believe at times). And to those who would try to belittle me with their narrow pity, I produce with a flourish my greatest triumph: Jesus rose again only once, while I, at the age of five, beat him hands down by doing so each and every day. Look at how my alphabet glistens. Am I not the one who makes the birds sing each morning? Yes, my daddykins was the Minotaur, the One and Only True and Real. So don't even think about running him down!

Indeed, as a kindergartner I could have unleashed the apocalypse, it was only my own desire that stayed my hand. And I restrain myself still. First, I must smother the blubbering creature inside me. That morning-bellyache-whiner who was blind to the gifts with which she was endowed, the riches heaped upon her. What am I to do with her? With this thumb-sucker, bedwetter, fuzz-from-the-woollen-blanket-plucker . . . a pudgy child who, as it turns out, in no way ever resembled me: the Consummate Simultaneous In- and Exhaler, the Concordant Mover in Time, the Completely Hushed Part and Parcel of the Pitch-Black Night! We mustn't spare her, but dash her to pieces, choke her and smoke her out, seeing as she is a massive disappointment, unworthy of the empire of Katiqiwa. A gross mistake and a big, fat nothing.

These are the things I wrote (only) recently. The blue ink rolled across the page as my hand recorded for me that which I didn't dare to know. How grandiose, how awesome it was, this Katiqiwa, and how so much of my later life has paled by comparison.

Am I making myself clear?

And what to say of those other nights, when I wake with a start or don't sleep at all, nights in which this, which was once so all-embracing, becomes pathetic, ludicrous. A farce.

The two-piece nylon baby-dolls, purchased by Anna Alida from the Raké fabric-store-of-the-same-name at Damstraat 44. The pot full of urine splashing over the top. Libby and I, I and Libby together in one room (one watching, the other crumbling, or vice-versa, rooty-toot-toot, who gives a hoot), Max sleeping his adolescent slumber in the adjoining cubbyhole, and the crucifix above the door with the shit-ass suffering, bloodily blood-spurting Jesus, not even the decency to turn his face to the wall, while the form below gets down to business, the purblind eyes and the nose deep in the rug's wool from which it sniffs up for all time the consecrated smell of little-people piss. Or the sprinkler present ever since in the Sacred Vagina, alias the butter-soft puss, providentially untouched while the other entrance (some entrance to a body can always be found) is explored profoundly and in-depth.

Then it becomes a snuff film. So depraved that the words and my being are, from then on, one and the same debauched thing.

Yes, sometimes I wander through the dark, my hands held out in front of me, in a wretched lust, a horrific craving, sensing that I have already passed out of existence: that I am dead, *lost*, molecules, *lost*, there where there is no gravity.

And the next time we're together again? Homeric laughter. In hilarity a hand holds up a torn-off leg or shattered forewing; does this belong to you? The cheerful rearrangement and reassembly of the various parts. Book bag, knee sock, ponytail. Snappy elastic bands with red gobstopper beads and Anna Alida or Henri Elias scraping a rat-tail comb across the scalp to make a perfect part. One arm around the waist to straighten the 'stop-jiggling-oh-god-can't-you-stand-still-for-once' torso with one fell tug.

Fidgeting in front of the mirror . . . it doesn't show at all! To be immortal, inviolable, invincible! To walk through a whirling buzz saw and not feel a thing. To be big as a mountain, thousand-titted, thousand-arsed.

All the things we can do, oh you'd be amazed! We are highly accomplished in being still as a mouse while penetrated, not making a peep or a cry. Loyal and staunch as tin soldiers. Alongside that, we can also simply cry when we scrape our knee. We eat our slices of white bread with granulated sugar and leave not a single grain behind on our plate. We waste nothing, waggle with our legs quite normally, we don't sit still, we giggle at everything.

Terror is a soundless thing that comes with padding tread. It asks nothing, conceals nothing. Is in complete agreement with itself. Along with its consort, the pure lust for life.

And here am I, crawling towards the spot that to this day exudes its fear-musk of yellow orchid, passion flower and dung, trying to catch sight of what I was there: the final doll inside the matryoshka, its slanted eyes painted on like commas. The doll you can't open.

TODDIEWODDIE'S GUEST HOUSE

SOMETIMES NAUSEA STRIKES me as though by magic, a dizziness as though I were rolling down a steep slope. And then I wonder whether it is really possible to tell this story. My mind wanders to the black, blackish-blue and emerald-green blowflies that brother Ninny burned to death on hot summer days, after having first pulled off their wings, zoof zoof, with exemplary speed and dexterity (how did he do that, anyway?).

'*Heeheehee*, now you guys aren't going anywhere. *Heeheehee*, now I got you.' Pressing the burning cone of his cigarette down on to them until it begins to hiss and siss, after which they spin round and round like minuscule dervishes with a sickening buzz.

Knock it off, knock it off! Die already, you!

I reprimand myself. 'It wasn't just one long string of misery or child-molesting, you know. Admit it, there were celebrations, parties too. Happy evenings when Anna Alida giggled as she let HEHH push her up the stairs after one glass of wine too many, shrieking nervously that she was going to wet herself laughing. ('*Hee-hee*, Henri, cut it out, you're going to make me pee in my undies') Afternoons when the most wondrous odours came from the kitchen (and the window in the kitchen door steamed over in a deep mist that you could write your name in), so that your very own flesh-and-blood heart soared with an oh, oh, homehomehome.'

Nothing is all a vale of tears. Even a Minotaur has moments when he contentedly picks from between his teeth a string of some cutlet or other. Moments when he rises to his feet and stretches with a yawn, before moving to the bookcase and taking down a lovely hardbound volume with a ribbon marker and opening it to Cicero's speeches, *o tempora, o mores!* Or nods off into innocent slumber on the couch, his mouth slightly ajar. Listen to that, *extremely* human snoring sounds . . .!

Besides: what to do with the fact that even strange, outlandish circumstances and bizarre situations can lend themselves to boredom and hilarity? It truly is a wonder, the things we find dead-normal, tedious or even downright laughable as children, when our reality is still defined largely by others. That wise, half-ripe, half-unripe age when we are open to a world that encompasses everything.

'You stinking little egoists, you pains in the neck . . . I'm going to knock your heads together and pound them up against the wall,' HEHH shouts, 'I'm going to tear you to pieces; I made you, I can break you too.' And we stand there giggling at the thought that he wants to bounce our heads off these shabby walls, and choke back our laughter as we consider the practical feasibility of his threats or the logic in his choice of words, confounding the whole time the knot of fear in our stomachs with that other, pleasurable tension you might feel while watching a horror movie.

We were lousy vermin. Pinheads. Pests.

That HEHH must also have seen himself at times as tiny and insignificant was something I didn't know back then, perhaps didn't dare to know. He was, after all, the creator of the labyrinth (that profoundly blacked-out reflection of his inner world and vision). Perhaps his contemporaries had locked him up in it once too. We expect them to be big, our gods. Powerful, impossible to topple. If they are not giants, who will protect us?

In *On Moral Fiction*, a book by John Gardner that I'd ordered for some reason during the time of the Big Freeze in the cabin in the woods (and of which I discovered as I read that I disagreed with the author on almost every page), there was one lovely, wry passage that was not only worth the price of the entire book but also prompted me to go out and buy Snorri Sturluson's *Edda* (a book that made me very happy).

"It was said in the old days that every year Thor made a circle around Middle-earth, beating back the enemies of order. Thor got older every year, and the circle occupied by gods and men grew smaller. The god of wisdom, Odin, went out to the king of the trolls, got him in an armlock, and demanded to know of him how order might triumph over chaos.

'Give me your left eye,' said the king of the trolls, 'and I'll tell you.'

Without hesitation, Woden gave up his left eye. 'Now tell me.'

'The secret,' the troll said, 'is: keep both eyes open!'"

I think back on the sacred rituals at Christmastide, which lasted almost one whole month in our Holbein household. Early December was already marked by a state of feverish anticipation. It started on 8th December (the feast of the Immaculate Conception of the Virgin), when HEHH installed his handmade, lead-foil screens before the three bay windows: a herd of deer, Mother Mary with her halo, a church . . . which turned that part of the room into a Gothic cathedral with ribbed vaults, lancet arches and flying buttresses . . . after which, on a Saturday afternoon, the gigantic Nordmann fir was hoisted and dragged up the steep stairs (Max pushing, Henri pulling, Ninny whooping) and, once the net had been cut open, magically unfolded and spread its feathery boughs wide.

After standing like that for a whole day, aristocratic and mysterious and as yet unfestooned, its crown brushing the ceiling in one corner of the room, it was time to hang the ornaments. The balls (which reflected both front and back rooms, but with a difference: rounder, more colourful and radiant), the blown-glass baubles that HEHH used both hands to remove from their marbled-paper packaging. Hand-painted houses in the snow. Blue and green pine cones. Siskins and robins with one speckled, downy tail-feather, two little silver birds with snow-white nylon plumes on a silver clip, and one stork, whose name was Peter (for all storks are named Peter, as Andersen's fairy tale shows us).

And lastly (for this, the stepladder was brought in), the coronation with the stately tree-top or Christmas angel, the tinsel amid the deep green as icicles on the branches, and the angel hair of finely spun glass with which the entire Caucasian fir was wrapped from head to toe in a delicate cobweb.

Only in the late afternoon of the day before Christmas came the solemn installation of the nativity stable. With the stone goats, stone sheep and the stone baby "Chee-zus", laid at the stroke of midnight in his stone manger beneath the soft-wood branches that spread their delicious odour of pitch and turned the whole room into an aromatic forest. Sometimes I would pick, from amid the boughs, one of those entrancing balls of amber resin. I would rub it fine between my fingers and sniff up its aroma with a feeling that I was floating and that a part of the forest had finally been let into our home.

While summoning this up before my mind's eye, I can and want to believe once more that HEHH was every bit as deeply divided as I and longed just as I did for that scission in which there was a father *and* a monster (and a father in whose arms I could hide from that monster)—and wonder whether I am better off in the knowledge that they were one.

The child who believes in myths and magic hankers after the old dichotomy. And remembers as well the joy, experienced freely and truly, of the soul's flight and the ability to attribute a mind to the smallest and humblest of things. Know this: I loved Henri Elias Henrikus Holbein, all of us adored our god.

*

"If we analyse the principles of thought on which magic is based," writes Sir James George Frazer in the hefty standard work *The Golden Bough*—a book about religion, popular customs and mythology that I went and bought in 1995, right after my first collection of stories (praised for its absurdism) came out, ". . . they will probably be found to resolve themselves into two: first, that like produces like, or that an effect resembles its cause; and, second, that things which have once been in contact with each other continue to act on each other at a distance after the physical contact has been severed. The former principle may be called the Law of Similarity, the latter the Law of

Contact or Contagion. From the first of these principles, namely the Law of Similarity, the magician infers that he can produce any effect he desires merely by *imitating* it: from the second he infers that whatever he does to a material object will affect equally the person with whom the object was once in contact, whether it formed part of his body or not."

I didn't stop to reflect on it at the time, but principles like these must have played a big part in our Holbein lives as well.

Accordingly, on a given day in August in the year 1974 (I was eleven), my sister Toddiewoddie (twenty-seven), second child of Anna Alida, dressed in nothing but a duster and bedroom slippers, fled with her two daughters (ages eight and five) from her flat in one of the aforementioned side streets of Damstraat, to seek refuge in the crisis centre run by Father Gerrit Poels, "Huize Poels" in Tilburg, a relief centre set up back in 1968 to help "the poor, the addicted, the confused and the desperate". Her hasty escape was part of a sad story that is perhaps best related as an allegory, anecdote or parable (one I have repeatedly used to my own ends as a riddle, conundrum or flashing red beacon) and the account (based on facts raked together effortfully) of a mirroring. Because my sister, the wild, licentious Toddie, who the inhabitants of our household always said was 'randy as a mink' and simply couldn't 'keep her knees together', and who, unlike the much more refined Henne, had been 'an unguided missile' ever since childhood, was now running away from a man.

In *The Night of the Hunter*, the 1955 film based loosely on a true story, self-ordained preacher Harry Powell (a spine-chilling performance by Robert Mitchum) meets a condemned bank robber in prison. To get his hands on his cellmate's fortune, he courts the man's widow. With the words LOVE and HATE tattooed on his knuckles, he beats and consoles the bank robber's two children, marries and murders the widow, and opens the hunt on the children.

Well then, forgive me my melodramatic and archaic words, for I have no others for it at this point: SUCH a hunter was THIS man as well. An EVIL and DANGEROUS creature who, in the guise of a reliable person for but a brief while, MOLESTED my sister's children. Who fiddled and twiddled with them on the crapper and who once, by night, when sister Toddie was suffering most grievously from her MENSES and tried to deny him access to her soft and tenderest TINDERBOX, set her bedclothes on fire and held her by the roots of her hair, pulling her head back in that way, and forced his way into her most cruelly. Who, when she dared gainsay him one morning (as was her wont), stood up from the breakfast table and without so much as a how-do-you-do poured BOILING OIL into the FISHBOWL on the sill (such that those nimble and innocent creatures in their globe of glass suffered a MOST WRETCHED DEATH before the eyes of her little ones . . .).

And how did my sister get to know this man? Where had she met him for the first time? And what was it that drew her to this AJMP, who would find himself convicted in 1984 to eighteen years' imprisonment and compulsory psychiatric treatment, and who in early 1972 moved in with her, straight from the penitentiary unit in Utrecht with the mythical name of "Wolves Square" (where he was serving time for a crime against property)? It remains, you could say, a mystery to this very day. A mystery, that is, for those who wish to view it through a veil of fog. To those who ask (but I'm the only one who does, I believe), Toddie always replies: 'Oooh, I don't know any more, that's one of those things I can't remember any more . . . that was such a horrible time . . .'.

But in those days my sister had apparently reconciled herself already to the fact that she would never find a partner of the unattainably high level of my father and her stepfather, HEHH, and as a young, uneducated, newly single mother had therefore blindly settled for whatever she could find on life's lower shelves.

There was an inner mirroring, and a vague outer one as well.

A. (Anton, "Ton", "Toni") J.M.P. had very pale, piercing eyes with bristly, transparent lashes; from a distance, if you squinted a bit, he could have passed for a respectable person. He always wore a suit, for example, a cheap white one to be sure with peak lapels and wide bell-bottom trousers, in keeping with the fashion of the day, and beneath that suit tight dress shirts in washed-out purple, lavender or yellow.

He had no job but would, once he had 'resolved a few private issues', go in search of one. Meanwhile, to fill the void, he took sway over Toddie's three-person household and almost immediately filled its every corner, nook and cranny from early morning till late at night with his all-pervasive presence. Like an octopus squirting toxic ink every time it moves.

The question I hear you asking now, of course, is how I know all this.

I know, first of all, because a wildly infatuated Toddie came to our home to present this Toni P. at the round dining-room table, *ciggy, ciggy, cuppacoffee, almond crisp* . . . whereby I somehow picked up on the way my mother narrowed her eyes uneasily as she examined this fresh new beau. And then went on to huff and puff that uneasiness away with one Caballero dark filter after the other.

'Henri,' I heard her say afterwards to my father (who had kept out of the conversation, focusing instead on his work of artistic and painterly merit, dipping his badger-hair brush in oil paint and laying out an artfully arched eyebrow in lamp-black here, placing a manicured nail on a graceful hand there, with a perfect crescent cuticle-moon in titanium-white, 'hands and feet are the hardest to get right, pay attention sometime, you'll see how often they bungle it'), 'what do you think . . .? He seems respectable enough . . .'

But the daughters from her first marriage were *her* factory seconds, *her* litter of kittens and *her* downfall and concern.

And secondly, because throughout those years (from roughly 1969 until Toddie's escape to Father Poels in 1974 and her stay at Holland's first women's refuge centre in 1975), from the moment in fact that I could first cover on foot the distance between our Holbein house and hers, I spent as much time at her place as possible. Despite what was about to happen in that low-ceilinged, three-room flat on Bandoengstraat and the things I would witness there . . . at Toddie's I felt welcome. Surrounded if not by safety then certainly by warmth. It's hard for me not to speak in lyrical, childish terms about what it was that made me, Kaj and later Libby too, gravitate towards her. Despite the violent pounding that would soon roll over her. Let me start by noting that Toddie was always very insistent about saying that I was 'no trouble at all'. That 'of -course-of-course' I could stay as long as I wanted, 'I think it's nice with you being around' (and, to my mother Anna Alida on the phone: 'No, I never even notice her, the kid's quiet as a mouse'). Or that at her house I could help myself to as much of the Honig macaroni—filled to the very top of the moiré-grey enamel pan, with its crumbly ground beef, spam, fried onions and tomato paste, with the plop-plop pearl onions and the crisp sweet-and-sour gherkins and big chunks of winter carrot—as I wanted, another helping and another and another until my eyes were crossed, until I burst, belched, busted, could eat no more. With her staring at me the whole time from across the table and the top of the big macaroni pan and breathing my name in amazement two or three times. 'Oh-my-gawd, you can really pack it away, can'tcha, someday you're going to eat me out of house 'n home . . .! You want another pickle?' Or the way up close she smelt of vanilla and butter. That, even though she lived on public assistance, her place was somehow always home to the wishing-table and the golden goose. That I was allowed to take whatever I wanted from her fridge without asking, and could avail myself of all the perfume bottles and flacons on her vanity table. Or, seated on the floral (peonies) upholstered stool, could rummage through her jewel box with the little ballerina on top that played '*Muß i denn*', looking for a chain with a locket, a charm bracelet or pierced earrings. I was allowed to walk around the house in her high heels.

And when I spent the night we would sleep together in her big, shiny double bed, made from blockboard shellacked in black and picked out in silver, a trough of sweat running between her belly and my back.

On the bare cement wall of my nieces' room was Bragolin's portrait of the crying gypsy boy. Sometimes, long before I knew what kitsch meant, I would open the door and stand there looking at it, strangely moved by the lone tear running down the child's cheek.

With a certain sorrow, I also think back on the days when I thought a warning would make any difference. In 1972, '73, '74, Anton, "Ton", "Toni" P. wasn't a murderer yet. And years later, by the time he showed up in a TV debate about compulsory psychiatric treatment to state that he needed chemical castration, because he simply couldn't help himself, *I'm just a poor boy, I need no sympathy, anyone can see, nothing really matters . . . nothing really matters to me . . .*, everything had already happened anyway and "Ton", "Toni" P. of Utrecht had headed north, and in Groningen "Ton", "Toni" P. (right after Toddiewoddie and her two young daughters had run for cover to the home for battered women) had met his new sweetheart, Hannie, and along with this Hannie "Ton", "Toni" P. had abducted nine-year-old Digna van der Roest, raped and murdered her . . . wrapped her little body in a trash bag and left it, tossed it, dumped it, chucked it into a culvert.

But between knowledge and action a chasm often yawns, and the knowing and the doing are linked in ways other than rational. And so there is something today, more than four and a half decades later, that still whirls around and around in my head. A cognitive loop in which I easily become entangled. For example, when I try to figure myself out as an eleven-year-old. How often, back then, did I proclaim at the top of my voice that things at Toddie's house were *not as they should be*? Deaf the whole time to that other, second voice, infinitely weaker and hidden deeper inside, which said that things at *our* house were not OK either . . .? And why did both my mother and Toddie come to me with their worries? What did they expect me to do? Then there was the way I noticed how my mother didn't trust this Toni P. How, that one, single time he came to our house, I heard her cross-examine him and listen to each of his answers with a thin, sardonic smile (blowing cigarette smoke on high from one corner of her mouth), and I *know* that after that awkward first acquaintance she spoke to me and me alone about the fact that he had said things that were odd. He had spoken of his mother in a way that was peculiarly abnormal. You could hear the hatred and the disgust right through it, she said, even though he acted as though he were in fact a loving son. I also know that she shoved aside these observations right away, but that the findings I handed her in the weeks and months to come, as though they were the results of some controlled scientific experiment, were things she told my father about too. In the hope, perhaps, that he would want to look into them, investigate them. Or at least add them to his lists of "things to think about". (One of his long lists of statistics, for example; folded sheets of graph paper pasted into his memo-book, on which he later kept track of Libby's and my menstrual cycles as well.)

The way I'm also certain that my father, HEHH, never bothered himself one iota about this testimony. Neither corroborated nor refuted it, only went on acting with astounding stoicism, as though no single conclusion or nervously presented thread of evidence of what was going on at Toddie's, no more than 750 metres from our own front door (the boiling oil in the fishbowl, the burnt sheets) could be of any import whatsoever. Perhaps he really didn't think it was important. Never, during that entire period, did I hear him say anything that reflected concern for Toddie or her children. I do know that there were *other* facts of consequence, ones that ranked higher in the hierarchy of things. And right away I hear them singing about my ears. Those phrases that must once have come from someone's mouth, but then went on dancing about of their own accord, like will o' the wisps, repeated without reticence or afterthought. That Toddie was a bitch in heat, for example, and always had been. A "walking cunt" who got pregnant as soon as you looked at her. While Henne was much more proper but also quite devious. Or that women could drive men crazy with their rotten comments and spitefulness, and by laughing at them, contradicting them, looking down on and belittling them. And the strange thing is, even though from a young age I could hear the discomfort, the injustice in these phrases, I always knew that they were *true*. And that the most terrible, most intolerable thing of all, for both this "Ton", "Toni" P. in his synthetic suits and for my father HEHH, was to feel ridiculed or not fully taken seriously. To not be awarded with respect or, at the very least, with an esteem leavened with dread.

And that was why, one Saturday, in a land far away and long ago, a heavy cut-crystal ashtray flew through a bathroom, smacked against the tiled wall so hard that a shard broke off and splashed into the water, and that shard pierced vertically the wrist of a seven-year-old, like the shard of ice in the heart of the boy in the "The Snow Queen". After which a man, a *floundering* man—now irate and grimly silent—whose comical slip-and-slide across the wet bathroom floor had inspired great snorts and giggles from his three children in the tub, roughly bandaged that little arm . . .

And that now and then a woman of fifty-five, when she looks up from her keyboard, for instance, sees that thin, delicate scar two centimetres long on her wrist and remembers the thrumming of her heart and the gauze winding around and around her heavily bleeding arm . . . the bandage thin, white, light as a feather . . . the blood red, bright and lovely . . . the dour 'sit still', the smell of aftershave, Tabac Original, from the white ceramic bottle with its little dark-brown diamonds, and the hands and fingers on her bare buttocks and, spreading these, boring in between them, like an apple corer. And her searing lust, welling up powerlessly . . .

Or in the way that there is still that soundless descent to the place where all of it and everyone is waiting. Look, there goes the amber-coloured tea, flying in a phenomenal arc from the glass teapot towards Toddiewoddie, that "cunt whore" with her "wet twat". Cries come from her throat. Her sea-green bathrobe falls open and she closes it again, ashamedly, over that belly of hers that is so familiar and dear to me. These are the days when Toddie wears inexpensive nylon underpants that she calls "French knickers". Of black and purple lace, sometimes crotchless and with a bow at the waist. On both sides of her navel, that deep, comma-shaped and mysterious hollow, are two faint, silver-white runnels. Signs of her pregnancies. Yes, of course, she had laughed at him. Scoffed. Ridiculed. Spoken the truth. *Made no bones about it.* I had been there, had seen it . . .

But this, when it comes to questionable behaviour, is not the final word as far as I'm concerned. There's something else worth mentioning too. I knew, just as Toddie and my mother did, that this hot-headed room-mate who had moved in head-over-heels was not to be trusted. And that they wanted to share their sense of impending catastrophe with someone and have it confirmed (preferably by HEHH). And that they tried to drown out their worries (the way you might, when confronted with a great din, emphatically go about making an even greater din yourself, knocking the lids off all the pots and pans, yanking all the tins, spoons, knives and forks from their cupboards and drawers, bangadaclangbang!). No, there was something else too, beneath that, behind it . . .

I know for a fact that both my mother and Toddiewoddie believed they could see through the weaknesses of the people they lived with. And because they were aware of those weaknesses, they also supposed they had control over them. Whereby their pride in this supposition overshadowed all the rest. Including their primal sense of self-preservation. That, I know, was also how it went with me. Despite my apprehension and alarm, there was not a single moment when I did not feel smarter and more capable than this "Toni" P., who did his best to hold sway from his seat at Toddie's dinner table (a replica of the one at our parental home) but couldn't put together a complete sentence for the life of him, whose speech was infantile, who had stubby fingers and clutched his knife and fork in his fists and gnawed his lower lip like a child as he wrote. Who could do nothing, make nothing, repair or accomplish nothing, but who flew into a rage at the drop of a hat. I took pleasure in dragging my books over there, piling them on the heavy coffee table, a wagon wheel covered with a tabletop of thick, lead-grey glass. The copies I'd smuggled from home of Turgenev's *Torrents of*

Spring and *First Love* (with its crackling cellophane cover) on top of the stack. And I felt satisfaction in the way he glared at me, exasperated, from across the room.

Oh, and I knew and learnt something else as well. You see, I had watched Toddiewoddie tease this Toni. Little jabs. About how his curly baby hair was growing thin, about the way he was starting to develop a belly . . . (a reasonable person, of course, would have taken these playful digs for what they were and responded good-naturedly or with a clever retort). She *knew* that the tiniest pinprick could cause him to explode. I had witnessed her sprinkling crumbs of vexation for him *even though* she had already felt the retaliations that could result from such infractions. But she just went on with it, even upped the ante in fact. Boisterous, vital, not the least bit timid. That she, with her pea brain, had beaten him at a game of cards, now hadn't she? And that even a moron could have told that he'd been cheating. Or that, for a self-proclaimed "mastermind" like himself, he'd got himself arrested and locked up *awfully* fast, now hadn't he . . . That if he dropped a penny into a piggy bank for every guilder of hers he spent, she'd be a rich woman today. Knowing all the while that there was a major chance that a fist would hit her in the eye, a pointy shoe slam into her side, that she wouldn't walk down the stairs but be thrown down them, bam-a-dam-bam-baddy-bam-bam . . . But she never, no never, applied the brakes.

'You pig!' she shouted, shortly after she'd caught him in the toilet with her daughters. 'You dirty bastard, jeeezus, you should have your head examined, you must be off your rocker . . .! No, listen, you're sick in the head! You got a screw loose, you're bat-shit, man . . . You've got something wrong with you upstairs!'

And the punches rained down and the pot full of scalding tea was thrown at her and her throat was pinched half-shut and the fucking happened. Hard, hurried, cruel: her just deserts . . . After which Toddie, picking nervously at her bathrobe, came to me for help. If maybe I could call the cops, because she didn't dare to.

Well then maybe you should have kept your mouth shut, I thought angrily, sorrowfully. Maybe you shouldn't have been so incredibly stupid, so reckless. I began to realize that nowhere did insight and wisdom reign supreme, and that I could rely only on my own devices. It was up to me to hammer out my own view of the world I lived in.

But there was something else I didn't understand at the time, something I learnt only after Henne died. That beneath all this lay triumph, a place where Toddie's laughter can be heard . . . like the smile worn by Daisy Domergue (Jennifer Jason Leigh) in Tarantino's *The Hateful Eight*. Whack! Another smack in the kisser. What a fight! But was it a fight between equals, or between unequals? After seeing that Western, I couldn't stop thinking about it. 'When I elbow you real hard in the face, that means shut up,' says the Hangman, who is bringing her to the gallows in a stagecoach along with another bounty-hunter, 'you got it?'

Furious, keeping her head down and out of harm's way, her hands still up in front of her nose, Daisy growls at him that she got it. You see? the Hangman nods at the bounty-hunter, who smiles broadly.

But then Daisy raises her head, her battered face fills the frame. Thick rivulets of blood are running stickily over her mouth and down to her chin. The bounty-hunter smiles at her and she looks at him, almost languidly . . . and then she does something odd. She smiles back at him and gives him a little, roguish wink. And he's startled, bewildered. Upon which, without taking her eyes off him, tauntingly slow, she licks the blood from her lips and gives him another wink like that before leaning back in her seat. Then she looks out of the window, sunk in thought and pain, tosses another glance at the bounty-hunger, and smiles again. An all-knowing grin.

That, I swear, is Toddie's grin.

The crime journalist Hendrik Jan Korterink published a book in 2015 with the prosaic title *Murderers in the Netherlands*. One of its chapters deals with the criminal couple Toni and Hannie, who sealed their pact of eternal, indestructible love right after Toddiewoddie had taken refuge with Father Poels.

In cool, clinical terms, Korterink describes the anything-but-rosy pasts of Toni (who was released on 4th May 2016) and his sweetheart (who died in detention). Toni had had three "fathers" and suffered repeated abuse. He was eventually taken away from his mother and made a ward of the state. In 1975 he met Hannie, whose life until then had been even more tragic, if such a thing is possible; there was incest in the family. The resemblance between her father's behaviour and that of her new hubby was striking. The book goes on to deal with the couple's mental states and capacities. The wife is said to have been apathetic and void of emotion, a "cold fish", Toni was averse to authority and displayed a "true pimp mentality". According to the court, the suspects had fairly low IQs, but were fully accountable for their actions; the charges levelled against them concerned the "most extreme brand of sexual offence".

'My husband liked to make Lolita photos,' Hannie reportedly said during the 1984 hearings.

'No, no, no, she made me, if she hadn't forced me I would never have done it. I would never have found out that I liked those kinds of games,' "Ton", "Toni" P. objected. By "games" he meant his own thirst for child pornography, to satisfy which his wife had even "brought in her own little nieces" and with which, according to him, he had first made acquaintance only after meeting her.

'Oh, you filthy liar,' I shout from here, from the comfort of my own living room. Because he was lying of course; his tears were crocodile tears.

I should know: I was one of those Lolitas.

*

Scientists in America have been working for years on an amazing project. They're investigating the most incredible substance of all: the chemical factor behind the smell of fear. In doing so, they make use of what we already know about ants. Ants communicate primarily by means of pheromones, which they emit to be smelt or tasted by other ants. In the early 1960s, new techniques for the microanalysis of natural chemical substances allowed the detection of these pheromones down to one-millionth of a gram, the amount normally carried by a single ant. Alarm pheromones released from the mandibular glands contain a mixture of ketone methylheptanone and alcohol methylheptanol, and are highly effective. The trail pheromone of the North American leafcutter (*Atta texana*), for instance, is so powerful that entomologists estimate that only one milligram of it (scarcely traceable in the laboratory, but roughly equal to the quantity found in an entire ant colony) is enough to lead a worker over a distance of 135,000 kilometres (three times around the planet).

I believe, no, in fact I know for a certainty, that a similar pheromone played a major role in my visits to and stays with Toddie. Scientific studies have shown that when one has been made into an object, forced to lie flat, not make a sound or move, one apparently gives off an odour. A reek of fear that goes with you. Perhaps even the scent of easy submission, because you have learnt that rapid capitulation is the best tactic.

Why do we so abhor the state of "victimhood" and the victim themselves? What is so reproachful, painful and shameful about it? Kafka described that abhorrence in *The Metamorphosis* and in "A Country Doctor" (in which a physician feels disgust for his patient). Japan's first modern writer, Ryūnosuke Akutagawa, talks about it in the "The Thieves", in which villagers place a woman who has died of the plague in an outlying hut, to avoid contagion. Walking past, the narrator sees dogs gnawing at the woman's limbs. Horrified, he moves on. On the way back, the dogs are still gnawing at her, and then he realizes that the woman is still alive . . . Her hopeless condition, however, elicits no pity, only loathing. As though she were responsible for the feelings the scene summons up in him.

It is that ultimate assent, along with the pestilential odour emitted by fear, that serves as an identifier.

That odour hung thick and heavy in our nest, and those olfactory molecules went with us everywhere. And—as can now be confirmed—there are others, I call them the "bigguns", who recognize those molecules, who home in on them, sniff them up. No matter how negligible the quantity, no matter how hard you try to conceal it.

For as long as I can remember, it has been my habit to buy perfumes . . . the antique walnut commode in my study is filled with them. Coco Chanel, Venezia, Roma, Guerlain's L'Heure Bleue and Mitsouko, Givenchy's Ysatis. It's never enough. At times, even these days, I jump up from my chair, race to the hall and down the stairs to stare into the oval mirror at my frightened face. I run my fingers through my hair. The breathing sticks in my throat . . .

Have you put it all away safely? Have you hidden everything well? Coming to pick the cherries . . . they always do. Just remember. With their finger-roots in all the cleft-crackslits, and you the blind, myopic four-eyes praying secretly at night for tits. Nudges from the grey beasts, nudges from the grey. Will come. Back and forth in time, they can. Will take. Not yet. One day. Will go away, but come back to pick the cherries. Something will be taken. Won't say when or what . . . Can smell where it is, smell the nervous passing wind . . . prtt, frrrt, flllt. In all chamber spaces and across light years of distance. The fear-fog of methane.

So that today my meanderings can be read clearly for what they were. A sporadically farcical series of attempted escapes, in which I followed the spoor of a scent that was already known to me and which—even though at Toddiewoddie's the trail mingled with the smell of fried luncheon meat and a bouquet of Tosca body powder—was one of direct recognizability and deep acquaintance-ship. An aroma that linked Toddie's guest house directly with its dark source: our house on Damstraat. And which, within a relatively short time (two years), showed itself for what it was: the mirroring of what, to me at least, must have been the Platonic Ideal, the Original. I had no idea of course (even though by then I considered myself so very wise and mature) that this Original was little more than a dark tunnel where I happened to find myself (some-times with and sometimes without piggies of the same ilk).

It's hard, after all—especially at that age—to see the things that overcome you as anything but directed at your own, particular person. Besides which, observations must needs be repeated in order to determine their validity. So that one can honestly and truthfully say: 'This situation corresponds significantly with one I experienced earlier.'

A five-year-old does a handstand, revealing a pair of baggy white undershorts. A pair of eyes begins to gleam and a voice says hoarsely: 'Goodness, she's becoming quite the little lady.'

'We have a litter of newborn kittens at our place, would you like to come and see them?' a woman asks a nine-year-old on 7th June 1982. The little girl climbs on to the back of the bike and, at the house on Billitonstraat, receives a glass of lemonade mixed with a powdered sedative.

'Take off your glasses,' a photographer in a centrally located, upstairs flat says to another, seated before the gas heater in her pretty dress and with her dark-brown hair bound in tight pigtails. 'My my, this way you're an awfully attractive girl to look at . . . Mr and Mrs Holbein, would you allow her to come to my house for a few photos?' (And soon, perhaps, her little brother and sister too . . .)

'Absolutely not!' you feel like shouting from history's far shore. Because you know what they really want to see in those photos: a far cry from the innocent snapshots that make their way into the family album. But not a soul can hear you there, of course. Yes, everything happened and had happened already, and since then the sirens have never ceased to sound. Sirens in the ears, drumbeats in the heart . . .

And Toddiewoddie leaves her house, on her soft cloth slippers.

Toddiewoddie disappears, vanishes, poof!

And yours truly, deeply alarmed but unsuccessful as yet in her attempt to shrug off the role of Cassandra, returns to the parental Holbein home. There she buries herself in books and devotes herself in deepest secret to the study, accessible to no man, of the correspondences and correlations, the mirrorings and foreshadowings between the two households known to her. Murmuring incantations and scratching out secret formulae, all the while applying herself to the drafting of possible routes of escape. To the search for masks, the whetting of rapier and sword and the laying in readiness of shears and augers. While dreaming of all the fantastic things she will do once she herself becomes a biggun.

I thought I already knew all there was to know, and all I had to do was try to arrive at a not-knowing. At times, though, I felt so weary. A hermit in a cloak of camel's hair who believed that the rest was only a matter of patience. Of sharpening the mind and honing a few skills.

In my naïveté, I'd failed to count on the time it takes to get away.

What life hands out is neither equitable nor particularly fitting.

'Cut her throat with the shovel,' Toni apparently said of Digna. And that she *kept on whining* that she wanted to go home . . .

Sometimes there is a great restlessness. Is it really possible to descend into that maelstrom? Looking for facts to cling to, like flotsam in turbulent water? Facts you'll only have to let go of again. Your memory is drawn into it, the nausea is like what overcomes you after eating cotton candy and climbing aboard the merry-go-round. The paint on that white pony is flaking fast, the pink unicorn isn't really alive, that bear will certainly tolerate no children on its back. It's all stuck together with iron staves, it spins and moves but goes nowhere. And at the centre stands the ticket-taker, a smile on his face. Knowing full well that there is colour that does not stick, pleasure that has never really been. The dolls that were moved around the house: Bella with her golden Rapunzel hair atop the mirrored linen closet in the parents' bedroom, Stella with her blinking eyes on the washing machine, Esther (blue sailor's suit with white bib) and Corrie (little loudspeaker "mrrama-mrrama" in her hollow breast) in the corner by the bathroom door. Making it more feasible and easier for a father to slip down a hallway . . . go back into a little girls' room . . . The facts that are confirmed, that turn out not to be merely nightmares or the eructations of a fraught and confused mind, but can be looked up in the form of dates, names, newspaper clippings, courtroom testimony. Of living people. Or of dead ones long gone and rotted, hiding underground in their wooden houses with roofs of stone or marble.

One by one they surface, pass in review. Paltry, worm-eaten, laughable . . . not at all well assembled, not when you view them up close . . . put together by clumsy fingers. Slapped together by folks with macabre little fantasies. Facts and pheromones that ruin your sleep and tell you that your days and nights were never actually all of one piece. That there were other moments too, drams drunk, sweets chewed, snapshots made (of weenies and woo-woos, of piggywinkle-piggies all in a row, nose to tail). And that among these murky, fearsome people of prey, HEHH was the best educated, most refined and Humbert Humbertian of all.

And probably, in that whole vortex, also the only bit of wreckage for you to cling to.

*

But here I must interrupt my discourse and draw your attention to a phenomenon that makes it singularly difficult to tell this story in clear, chronological fashion. For a chronological narrative, after all, clear thinking is a prerequisite. A capacity I did not possess for a very long time.

Having said before that HEHH was a master of deception, because he could make even that deception vanish like snow in the sun (when I said he was a conjuror, a wizard and a shaman, I was speaking in the most literal way: he could shift shapes miraculously, take on various guises and be in different places at the same time), even more extraordinary was this: he could make me vanish too, his greatest act of legerdemain, and make something else appear that looked like me but nonetheless was something different . . . Seeing as it is virtually impossible to say when this trick was performed for the first time, it behoves me then to jump to the last time something like that happened . . . and so return to a moment when yet another major slice was cut from my consciousness. An occasion, not coincidentally, when I tumbled to the trick itself. Even though it took me half a lifetime to come to grips with the changes made.

1975 turned out to be a remarkable year in every way. One in which the Arriera Queen, her lungs black with smoke, their insides coated with tar and pitch, was admitted to a sanatorium for respiratory cases. A white building just outside town, with lots of glass; a greenhouse amid the trees, in the forests of Zeist. There she stayed for several months. We remained behind with Henri Elias and visited her as often as we could, availing ourselves of public transport—the regional buses of the Central Netherlands (he did not own a car)—or the bike.

It was the second time that my mother Anna Alida drifted away from us, and this time she drifted even further than before, because her place was taken. There was a cavity, an empty space in the nest, and it had to be filled.

Henri was—you see—inconsolable. Awfully, so awfully inconsolable . . .

And there are spectral memories of us, of Libby and me, in the blue parental bedroom where we were arranged according to the rules of the tangram. Henri the black square, yours truly the triangle, adjacent to or imposed upon, so that the figure ended in a sharp point, and Libby the (anomalous, inconsonant) little red disc a bit further away, on the door side of the conjugal bed. Anna Alida's green satin peignoir on a hook beside the mirrored cabinet.

Within that, reflected for those who dared to look: the new family structure. Libby with her warm blonde head on the pillow. Her mouth open, spittle dripping on to the pillowcase, perhaps an occasional wakening and a nervous glance to one side before being urged back to sleep. And yours truly and the Minotaur in a configuration that was oh-so-much-more aligned, so much more accentuated.

The expanse of ice began and spread out from there. With the grooves and zigzag scratches of a furious skater.

Kaj at early morning, a stupefied and inaccessible creature of unbearable softness. His pet turtles had died, he said, he found them floating on their backs in the aquarium and flushed them down the toilet (later it turned out they had been hibernating), and the hall from this angle and this perspective endlessly long, like the World Serpent in the *Edda*.

What had once begun came to a close, then and there. All roles played out, all pieces shuffled, all tangram rules broken. The square pressed upon the triangle, the disc squeezed from the rectangle . . . And downstairs by the oaken table, yours truly accepting the banknotes: three of twenty-five guilders each, for the hotly coveted Palomino trousers the colour of smashed berries . . .

Heathcliff, it's me, Cathy . . .

In any case. Henri said, there was nothing to cry about. And I was already twelve by then. So he was probably right.

I don't think Anna Alida knew that I had turned into a body-snatcher in her absence. She lay in her glass coffin, beneath her white sheets, with a view of the forest, wakened and greeted by a male nurse with fresh pills of all shapes and colours, and kissed on the cheek by Henri, who smuggled forbidden cigarettes to her during evening visiting hours. Caballero, unfiltered.

The protagonist of my father's only (and unpublished) novel, "Pinacotheca for the Blind" (bound in light-blue cardboard, 300 pages A4, typed, with holes punched left for the metal binder), is a young man, Paul, who winds up in the arms of a much older woman. Paul is a sensitive, blond, introverted boy of great intelligence and with a singular talent for drawing. The woman is blind—I've forgotten what caused her to lose her eyesight—and he paints paintings: he does it all for her, he portrays her on every canvas, his entire life is one huge worship service, an attempt to kneel before this woman as his muse and goddess in order, once the altarpiece is finished, to disappear from the world into her embrace, like the child gobbled up by the grown-up.

Reality was less charitable than that.

Henri Elias Henrikus Holbein completed his novel shortly after Anna Alida returned from the sanatorium, in the same summer of that Jubilee year of '75 in which we moved to the green-rolling pastureland of a suburb and forgot about Toddie. And in which Henne, who had sought, found and occupied a house nearby along with her husband and children, came to visit on occasion. She always sat on the edge of her chair, coat still on, ready to leave at any moment. My memory of her is clear, in her white llama jacket with fringe, perched on the brand-spanking-new easy chair in the corner by the door. An oak-wood behemoth, its bright-red upholstery crawling with black-embroidered roses, part of the set that went with the three-piece suite. A suite of furniture that my mother, who regularly expressed the hope that our move to Nieuwegein would provide her with 'a clean slate', and to whom my father supplied a generous budget for household effects, had picked out along with Max: it looked like they'd found it at an auction of the Bluebeard estate.

SWEETS FOR MY SWEET

NOT LONG AFTER all this foment and my own personal state of panic, I descried in myself the first burgeoning of a line of thought that would grow in the course of the years into a rugged vine, and that went roughly like this: all right, maybe once everything was hunky-dory, but now it's shot, kaput, so don't go crying over spilt milk, just do what you can to lead a good life someday. In doing that, keep your eye on the line that separates the quick from the dead, the awakened from the slumbering, the hopeless from the helpless—and concentrate on what you want to achieve and where you want to end up. In order, should you arrive there someday, to pour yourself a glass of ruby-red wine and raise a toast to having come this far, and to the pleasingly large gap between you and the stragglers. Even if, to that end, you've had to lie a little, or a whole lot a little. Better off, after all, to look like someone who's *always* drunk ruby-red wine from a lovely crystal chalice.

And should a nasty situation arise (one that reminds you of something else), then remember that there is a limit to the amount of grief a person can claim as their own, and that you can't take everyone along with you into that satisfying and comfortable chamber. If, for the time being (and under whatever shadowy pretences), you've been admitted to the hall of tapestries, that doesn't mean that *everyone* is allowed in along with you. Maybe you'll get away with leaving a pair of muddy shoes at the door. But two or three or four pairs—of other people's muddy shoes?

The best thing you can do then, therefore, is learn to drink the ruby-red wine; sip by sip, little finger extended primly, until you forget . . .

Red wine, it's commonly known, tends to facilitate that. Ruby-red wine does the trick.

One's all right,
two's too many,
three is not enough . . .

It was around that same time that Toddiewoddie was raped. No charges were pressed; no one was willing to back her. She became pregnant and put the child up to be adopted at birth. All this came about in Deepest Secret, for by then Toddiewoddie was already Taboo. As long as she found herself in that terrifying plight, no one talked about her. One can almost imagine that, at the place where she remained during her confinement, her food was passed to her at the end of a long stick, the way they once did with the unclean, and that they wrapped her each night in black sheets. We never went to visit her. During labour, too, she was alone. I didn't see her again until 1977.

It must also have been around the time of our move and Toddie's banishment (and my own "freeze") that I began to occupy myself with reading horror stories and making rather disturbing drawings, which I scratched in gouache or India ink on snowy-white pages with pointy dip-pen and a great feeling for detail. Chopped-off hands. Severed heads. Intestines bulging from abdominal cavities in bunches, like garlands of flowers . . . blood dripping from fingers, slit throats, sundered arms and legs (and oh, lest I forget: the tortured ones were always female).

'*Magnifique, magnifique*,' oozed the art teacher at the prep school where HEHH dropped me, the seventh-grader, each morning on his way to work from our New Arcadia, before wending his way to the Centre for Data Analysis on Varkenmarkt. First we took the crowded, bright-yellow commuter bus past the fields and steppes that separated the no-man's-land of our abode from the city. After that, heel-toe-heel-toe together down the morning-silent streets and across the canals of dark water to the grand prep-school building. Where the art teacher with his puffed-pancake face, his black hair and handlebar moustache, turtleneck and black-velvet jacket with lapels dusted in dandruff—like a bloated replica of Salvador Dalí—hopped up and down and uttered orgiastic cries. 'Ach' (hop, hop, hop) 'just look at that, would you . . .!' (hop, hop, hop). 'Reminiscent of nothing less sublime than *The Garden of Earthly Delights* . . .'

As a matter of fact (and he must have reckoned the same), I had access to more than enough sources of inspiration. Had I not pored over the illustrations in the art books (which HEHH brought home from the big discount bookstores like De Slegte), these days by the abundant light from the windows of our new Through Lounge? The Aubrey Beardsley print of Salomé clutching the bleeding head of John the Baptist? Or Caravaggio's *Judith Beheading Holofernes*? And *L'Apparition* by Gustave Moreau, with the halo round the floating head of the prophet? To say nothing of Gustave Courbet's *Le Sommeil*? Two young, nude females—one brunette, the other with copper locks—in a lustful embrace on a mussed bed . . . Or the flagellation frontispiece, also by Beardsley? As well as Klimt's cool-yet-sensual women? Or Egon Schiele's sickly-coloured females with their mollusc-grey pubes? But also . . . and where had I seen them for the first . . . at Toddie's house, perhaps, or in Max's shadowy cubicle . . . (for how familiar it all was, how very recognizable)—the violent "adult pulp-art comics" with revealing titles like *Jacula, Meanwhile Back at the Morgue, Oltretomba, Frigidaire, Cannibale*. Or just *Terror! Horror!*

Torture-erotism rife with severed breasts served up on platters like lotus blossoms. Writhing bodies, wrists riveted into iron shackles or bound with coarse rope. And sometimes the respite of a goddess of vengeance. Vampirella! with her shiny black boots, majestic thighs, red-latex sling suit and quick wits. She hailed from the planet Drakulon, where all the rivers ran with blood. (LOOK OUT! SHE'S WAITING INSIDE THIS FIRST COLLECTOR'S EDITION . . . FOR YOU!)

The reading continued, more apt, more enticing . . . after all, I was all grown-up now. Another two years, no more than that, and on it went to the works of Marquis de Sade. And the writing began. Even though I still had to find all the words.

Those who looked at me saw above all a mini-courtesan. Busy arranging, organizing . . . with educating Libby (miming it for her: 'put your hand around it, not too tightly, then move it steadily up and down') and with developing stoicism of spirit. *Hustlin'-bustlin'*, doing my best to ignore the *umph-umph-umph* of the beat as I visited bars and discos, dressed up and all decked out on my own.

In any case, there you had me: Pallas Athena, in full armour, sprung full-blown from my father's forehead.

In 1976 or '77, soon after Max officially moved out and Libby moved into his virtually unslept-in room that still smelt of "new house", so that she and I were sleeping in separate rooms for the first time in years, I asked for a lock on my bedroom door. My bed stood straight across from it, and in those days I slept very little. I was an obsessive puzzler, always doing crosswords and solving cryptograms. But the Minotaur no longer visited me. (Perhaps he went on for a time searching the stripped rooms of our former home, knocking desperately on walls and floors in search of the girl-thing of yore. Or clawing like a madman at the wallpaper.)

He didn't seem to follow me to Groningen either, where in 1978—as high-school dropout (and hunger artist: I had developed the "fashionable disease" anorexia nervosa)—I moved into a little mustard-coloured room to start part two of my life.

It could be he was with Libby.

And so it grew, up and apart. Henne, Toddie, Libby and I. Without language, with no shared vocabulary. Waking with a start at the same hour, waiting, watching ('I tear a splinter off the bedframe, hold it pointed at the door . . .'), bound together by what Einstein called *spukhafte Fernwirkung*, spooky action at a distance.

Allow me, if you will, once again to slice my way through the multi-layered *spekkoek* of time, in which all things existent, occurrent and previous are so tightly pressed together; I'm afraid there is no other way. I mentioned earlier that our Holbein cosmos, savage and inaccessible as it was but never unlettered, was home to a variety of tongues. The idiom of the "back neighbourhood", seasoned with slang and snippets of Sinti, Romani and Yiddish (*tokhes*, *temeie*, *gawsones*, *dummkopf*, *achenebbisj*, *stoosh*, *tsores*, *chajes* and *tinnef*) existed alongside the specific language of mathematics (what Simon Stevin in the sixteenth century had given the name *wiskunde*, "*kunst van het gewisse of zekere*", the art of what is known or what is certain), of chemistry and informatics. The idiom of precepts, commandments and papal or Holbeinian decrees ('You stop talking to your mother like that or I'll wring your neck!' 'Nobody around here has anything to want, except me!' 'You're all a bunch of whited sepulchres: lovely on the outside, rotting away on the inside!') sounded alongside "technical" or scientific German, the silver of Church Latin and the gold brocade of "aristocratic" French.

Those languages fascinated me. The way they collided, scraped together, disharmonized.

Yet beside this linguistic fare there was also nourishment for the body. With HEHH as fixer *extraordinaire*.

Though Anna Alida prepared our workaday meals of vegetables, potatoes and meat (chops or a meatball), from HEHH's hand came (on Friday, Saturday and Sunday) the ploppy vanilla pudding, the creamy bavarois with its candied peel, raisins (wrinkly and full, like the blowfly rumps Ninny left behind on the windowsill) and bitter almonds to grind to grit against the roof of your mouth.

He fixed the chocolate pudding (poured warm from the pan into ceramic bowls where it set immediately, fat and mysterious chunks of cacao beneath the earth-brown skin) and the whipped cream crackling with sugar on the beater (two whisks in the bowl, one for Libby and one for Kaj, a wooden spoon for yours truly). Friday shopping brought home the pink, whole white and powdered aniseed comfits from De Ruijter (purveyor to Her Majesty); the oblong ones with the greyish-black anise seed inside them that stuck between your teeth. The chocolate sprinkles from Venz: manna raining down on white bread from the aluminium spout. The jars of Hero strawberry jam, Nutella hazelnut paste and packets of real butter . . .

And when we Holbeins became more prosperous and the grinding poverty of our predecessors had long been replaced by that middle-class prosperity that is expressed in foodstuffs, on Sundays there were currant loaves with almond-paste filling (the first slices still void of that pasty heart of nuts and sugar), and tutti-frutti to go with the poultry or the roulade (always braised dark on the outside, with crackly crust and basted with treacle or sprinkled with soft brown sugar before entering the oven).

Indeed, meat on the table every other day. Thick, greasy gravy and *magnificent* sweets. All of us were mad about these delights, which were meant above all for our mother. But she had chosen, so we could too.

They soothed, they calmed. We stole them too.

There goes Kaj, tiptoeing through the kitchen. He presses the plates full of precious cargo to his chest, climbs the stairs warily.

Our family was absolutely wild about sugar.

Perhaps then you can imagine the willpower it took to refuse all this and send one's plate back to the kitchen untouched.

The way I began to do, a year after moving into our new house.

The way Henne had done.

To this day I don't know whether the way Henne's life ended was her surrender, or her revenge. A "fuck you!" to the world, like a raised middle finger. Or the tumbling of a parched plant, so light the wind blows it thither. I know the "outcome" or the "end result" of her life, but still it wakened the sleuth in me. Her slow starvation, the refusal to be taken to the hospital, her hermetically sealed existence for years on end with that defective son with his smile enigmatic as the Mona Lisa, or Velazquez's buffoon, Juan de Calabazas. During her funeral he held a black-haired Barbie doll in his hand.

At this point, an anecdote concerning one of the few things I actually know about Henne's childhood seems appropriate. One day in 1958, HEHH came home from work with the announcement that a new girl was coming to live with them. Not just any girl, no, a very pretty girl with long black hair, a slender figure, a cute face—with an elegant little nose and lovely black eyebrows. She was to be given a room of her own and from then on Henne and Toddie were to share everything with her. Toddie reacted blandly to the news. But the prospect of this new arrival caused Henne to tense up, for weeks she slept and ate poorly. In March 1959 the moment came; the newcomer would arrive that very day. They were not allowed to stay home from school to meet her, no, they would see her only when school was over. When they came home, Henne hesitant, sick with anxiety, Henri looked them over closely. On top of the big TV set was a copper stand holding, in all her elegant and rigid perfection, Mattel's very first Barbie, with her pitch-black nylon hair.

The story of Henne's pettiness was one Henri loved to tell. He was proud of having thought up this bit of theatre in which she, as he must have predicted, would play perfectly her role of the child devoured by jealousy.

When did Henne start dyeing her hair raven-black? She did so until her death, and denied it to her dying day. I barely remember her without coal-black tresses down to her buttocks. Only when most of the neighbourhood children began to chant, 'There's the wicked, wicked witch!' whenever she came outside did she shear it off at last.

After the death in 2005 of our mother Anna Alida, who had been the last to see my sister's household with her own eyes, Henne and her son, our nephew, came to inhabit a secret place. The darkened temple ruins of the ill, the handicapped and needy—a shadowy region completely outside the economic life, the production and consumption processes of the city. With only Ninny going to visit occasionally, puttering about her like a worried doctor: 'Listen Henne, are you sure you're eating enough? Are you taking good care of yourself?'

After her death, I've been told, her house was a rubbish heap, an Augean stable. She had long ago stopped all attempts at cleaning house or dusting. Her son—our nephew in residence—was a firm believer in the comprehensive tasks of the maternal caregiver. Order was found only in her fridge, where a lone bulb shone on nothing but empty racks.

In the last years of his life, HEHH occasionally went by bike to visit her, for a cup of coffee. I imagine she served it to him properly, with two lumps of sugar on the side. At times I wonder whether she realized that she had become a burnt-out match. You know, one of those safety matches that's all black and crumbly. What is one supposed to do with it now? It's useless. As a child I always put warped matchsticks like that back into the Säkerhets Tandstickor box, with its picture of the swallow with frayed wings. Henri hated it when I did. But even as a tot I was unable simply to throw things away, I waved goodbye to my own bowel movements, prey to a separation anxiety that my surroundings found both inexplicable and hilarious. 'Bye, poopie, bye-bye!' What would happen to my turds now? Who would care for them? Only later did I become careless and sloppy, I forgot everything.

Stupid turds. Stupid matches.

Sometimes I wonder how it would be if someone other than myself told this story, recounted this history, Max for example, or Kaj. You see, I am becoming increasingly aware that my life is finite, just like other people's, and that I must make haste; it's as though I can see the end approaching, straight through the clouds of dust on the horizon. What's more, I've always been slow to fathom the lives of others, even though they return regularly in my dreams and loom up before me like ghosts as I write. Only then does it become clear that I have, in fact, retained what I seemed to have forgotten during the day, during the hours when I am not writing.

Yes, Henne Fire, there you are in the kitchen on Damstraat, old and at the same time excruciatingly modern, just as I myself am now old and at the same time excruciatingly modern. You're making sandwiches for us. 'Who wants butter on their bread?' You dance with our mother, and take the lead. Drive your car (you're the first Holbein woman with a licence). Claxoning cheerfully as you steer around corners, hitting the horn, hruurrur-rurrhh, honk.

'Say whatever you like, but I was a good daughter,' you say. A statement that reverberates inside me like a line from some kitschy duet.

Grovelsong, skivvy and slavey.

What is fidelity? What is loyalty? Some say it's a moral alliance. A cleaving to a union, bond or obligation, the prospect of expulsion from which is tantamount to the most drastic and unthinkable of rejections: exile.

In memories ghostly and oppressive (because they are a part of the gentle and tender ones too), I see my father in his wrinkled pantaloons and paint-flecked shirt, standing beside Max and Kaj as they hatch a plan and carry out some boys' thing. A red-papered piece of firework stuck deeply inside a dog turd or tied to a bottle. A rocket made from a cardboard tube filled with gunpowder. An ochre-coloured metal car on a steel zip-line running to the hardware store across the street (where Kay's best friend lives).

How HEHH smiles, his face lights up, how he is truly there.

Welcome, bidden.

There are days, Wednesday evenings in summer or autumnal Thursdays (thinking of strawberries atop the rusks . . . the door open to the little tiled terrace, and us, looking at the play of light and shadow on the walls . . . of the stores, lighted and open for late-night shopping, and Anna Alida, Toddie and Henne's excited anticipation) when I remember how I almost believed, and wanted to believe, that it was all perfect, that it could all have been perfect. Max and Kaj tinkering and dabbling about at their workbench, busy generating "electrickery", the whipped-cream beaters on the counter . . . and that we lived in the best of times, the best of families . . .

And then I know that memory (Mnemosyne) and Huginn and Muninn (thought and remembrance) are cruel.

Maybe I myself am cruel.

I think back on HEHH's final overtures towards our mother. She couldn't bear him any more. When he placed a hand on her shoulder, she would shiver and a cold tremor ran through her.

Or how on occasion he tried to join the special community formed by us, his youngest children, by telling us crusty old jokes. About a man who wants to learn how to ride a camel and receives instructions from a nomad: to make the animal run, he has to say, 'whew', and to make it stop he must say, 'A chicken is not a pineapple.' And how HEHH expanded maddeningly upon this simple joke (the camel trots stoically for hundreds of kilometres across the Sahara, trotting, trotting, slogging straight across Morocco, Mauritania, Egypt, sandstorm, burning sun) we'd all heard before anyway, until finally he gets to the part where the man panics as he sees a huge ravine up ahead and realizes he's forgotten how to make the camel stop. Only to end up (his eyes agleam and riveted on us, his restive audience) with the long-expected but far too tardy 'A chicken is not a pineapple!', right at the brink of the ravine. And with the camel-driver pulling out his handkerchief, wiping his forehead in relief with a loud 'whew' and the camel promptly plunging into the abyss.

By that time Kaj and Libby had already left the room. While I, my eyes fixed on the crumpled cotton cloth that HEHH had used by way of illustration to wipe his own forehead (and that had so surprisingly defied the principles of time and space), had already taken my mental leave.

Hence, perhaps, this hesitation, this guarded pace as I approach the old room. For that is where he resides, the venerable Minotaur. He is trying to do a puzzle, solve a riddle, a mathematical problem. After a while he senses that I'm staring at him and turns. His eyes are sombre.

'Ah,' he says. 'Is that you, girl,' and I feel his loneliness and want to sit with him, because I want to help him solve that riddle. And I roll up my ball of yarn and tuck it away.

Into the woods, into the woods we go . . . if only I could go to the woods to walk and see the earth stretch out gently in front of me, endless, endless, for no other reason but to make it possible for me to walk in those woods. I think I could grow there and become big as the trees, could walk their slow gait with them, vertical as it is horizontal. In the woods I think I'd be able to breathe. Notice that I am not talking here about "The Forest". (My woods provide you with a clear view of the sea, my woods climb and cover mountains, my woods move.) We would move ahead together in step, the woods and I, and I would run my hand over its bristly fir back, like that of an enormous beast. A wild and graceful beast of extraordinary intensity. I would be a child of the woods, but why only a child? I would be the woods themselves and listen to the gong of our shared heart, and every ring in every tree would be precisely one, single beat of that gigantic heart.

*

One time, when I was about twenty-two, I saw the Minotaur afoot. By that time Libby would have left home as well. He had emerged all the way from his labyrinth and walked in total isolation down the beach, at a distance, without speaking, without for a moment the expectation of human contact. With every step his tail swept away his own hoofprints, then the potholes he'd made filled with water. His tail powerful as that of an ox, his head dark upon his muscular shoulders. He looked the very sight of perfect desolation. No sound escaped his inhuman lips, only formulae. The creature itself, intelligent, shrewd, seemed to understand that it was not fully human.

That was on a Tuesday, the loneliest day of the week.

I confronted my father on two occasions. The first was in my youthful guise as a thirteen-year-old. I stood in front of him in his office on Varkenmarkt (where he, as usual, was sitting at his desk) and pronounced my *noli me tangere*. Father, touch me no more, for I have known a man.

The second time, I was twenty-six. I was studying liter-ature, had just become a single mother, and was teaching classes at a regional training centre. A training school for adults. I suffered under myself, suffered under my own behaviour, and was rattled and hounded by the nasty dreams I mentioned earlier, which—because I'd been eating normally again for a few years—sprang up in my brain like toadstools from a toxic mycelium. Growing in number and frequency, they became entangled with my daily life and trickled through into my actions. Hallucinative images. I stared at them, transfixed like Alex in *A Clockwork Orange*, while teaching my students, who were themselves fleeing wars and persecution. Or at my flat, while prepar-ing a one-pot meal for myself and my young daughter. Or dozing on the couch, across which I had draped—oh snugness! oh ambience!—a grand foulard in paisley print, my schoolbooks open on my lap, with, in the margins, the notes for the paper I was writing about Edward Bond's

Lear. 'Listen, Cordelia. You have two enemies, lies *and* the truth,' underscore, underscore . . .

Fascinated, yes, but each time too with a frightened abhorrence of what my own mind dished up for me unawares. And with such gratuitous, off-putting details! A stream of atrocities in living colour. Vivid and often (like in the works of de Sade) preposterously impossible. Pompous, ridiculous, with too many convulsions, too much squirming, smear and slime. Skinless horses stumping down empty streets, sweating blood and lymphatic fluid. Smashed organs slithering away like jellyfish under the soles of my feet. Operating rooms beneath blinding lights, with the surgeons' arms plunged armpit-deep into their fettered patients . . .

Help me, help me, I am no longer of sound mind.

It must have been 1990, that second time. The Berlin Wall had already fallen, but Mandela was still in prison. I had called HEHH, arraigned and summonsed him. 'There's something I need to talk to you about, Father.'

One hour later we were standing by the bushes just outside the entrance to Cityplaza, the throbbing retail heart of Nieuwegein. Bushes so intensely green that I could see each individual leaf, as though they'd been painted by Pyke Koch, one of those magical-realists of whom HEHH was so fond. One of those images that possess no depth; things in the foreground have the same solid contours and are painted with the same precision as what lurks in the background, leaving no distance and therefore also no time or space between events. He held the handlebars clenched in his hands as he said he recalled none of the things I asserted. His memory was very bad, he said, funny, it was like a sieve. He was already an old man by then. Asthmatic. The backs of his hands were speckled with liver spots and I heard his laboured breathing and looked at his grey, baggy trousers. During those few minutes we stood there, I may have nodded and smiled. Before he climbed on his black gent's bike and cycled away, back home, to my mother.

I stood there, didn't move.

He had given me the Andersen book.

When our reality finds itself at loggerheads with our hopes and desires, we have various strategies at our disposal. In addition to applying selective perception, we can also modify our former convictions. Unconsciously, we then often do what a lawyer does in a professional capacity: collect evidence and present it in such a way that it best supports the side of the case we wish to affirm. A constructed and selective version of the facts, offering us the best overlap with the reality we long for. In fact, we rewrite history. We profit from the lie. It resolves something for us, redeems something on our behalf.

There is evidence to show that he was a man of worth.

*

Being now so far along on this journey, the objective of which is to salvage that which has been sundered in the course of the years and thrown overboard as unfit and unwanted, it is perhaps worth pausing for a moment to consider the death of Henri Elias Henrikus Holbein and what took place thereafter. HEHH's passing transpired within the space of a few minutes, in the early hours of a sunny October morning in 2001, the year of the Twin Towers. Anna Alida called me and said, in a voice full disbelief, that he had just now collapsed in her arms, quite calmly. 'Papa is dead,' that's the way she put it. We had invited the two of them to our house later that day, to have dinner with Oleg and me, and we were about to leave for the market with an extensive shopping list (veal roulade, fresh peas, potatoes, and eggs, sugar, milk and flour for the crêpes we'd be having for dessert). It was only a month before this that the two planes had drilled their way into the towers. But Henri Elias, who was very old by then, was too distrait to pick up on much of it, let alone become upset. He spent most of his days sleeping on the couch, and no 9/11, in fact no event whatsoever, was going to change that. This to the great irritation of our mother Anna Alida, who had begun speaking ever more loudly (regardless of whether he was asleep or awake) about her plans for after his demise (later, soon, any time now), as though the years that lay between had not really been lived and were, as far as she was concerned, neatly boxed up and stored away somewhere.

Like me, Henne hurried that morning to the little senior citizens' flat where Max, Libby, Kaj and I had helped them move one year earlier. That day, Henne was the same age I was when she died. And I remember quite perfectly the attention and care with which we, the Holbein daughters (with the exception of Toddie, who stayed away), saw to the body that lay on the bed before us like a carved sarcophagus (the neatly manicured hands, the golden band of the wedding ring, the bared genitals like strange fruit, the face inscrutable as a stone).

We didn't say much. Hand me the towel, would you, is there any more fresh water, a clean washcloth? Shouldn't we shave him? Perhaps the corpse passed a little wind. Of that we said nothing either as we washed him, dabbed and dried him. In his coffin he was surrounded by stuffed animals from his grandchildren, rolled-up drawings and letters in colourful envelopes.

I dream sometimes that I go to his grave and dig it up with my bare hands.

Something else occurs to me, by the way, with regard to his passing. It would be preposterous to claim that there was only devotion and devotion alone. Why else would we have kept him above ground and in a house with little in the way of air conditioning, until the tip of his nose (a characteristic element of his face) turned black and his body began decaying amid the stuffed animals? Why else hang over him like withering orchids, growing, twining, twisted and contorted, warped? Yes, our love had a dimension to it that was sickly and stemmed from an all-too-great attachment. Still, that fails to explain our peeking and peering inquisitively through a fissure beyond the boundaries of death.

Our god it was, rotting away there during those (six!) nights aboveground. Our god turning to wilted flesh that was about to fall from the bone. And there was to be no resurrection or reawakening. No victory or triumph, only a queasy sort of nausea as we listened to the cells' cries of distress, their fear of disintegration, of the immense, ghastly space between the atoms. Their realization (without thinking, for there can be no more thought) that an all-inclusive "self" has ceased to *be*. And the brief flickering, felt in unison and down to the nucleus of each and every cell, that said self had been something artificial, a cultural construct.

Mauriac, Diderot, Delacroix, Baudelaire, all those formulae . . . where are you now, where are—?

Yes, a great frenzy and even fury in the cells, even in our own, seeing as all cells derive from others. *Omnis cellula e cellula.*

And sorrow. Soaring all the way to the heavens. For Henri, who made a good soup and had lovely hands. Who wanted to be an artist.

Why, then, bewail a childhood so filled with powerful impressions? Do we human animals really think we're so special? Always talking about back when we began. Whence this whole fateful assumption that our first years on earth are to be filled with happiness, warmth, love and tenderest solicitude? Isn't it enough for us simply to exist? Ask any given human about their childhood and the floodgates will open. And the things that come gushing out! Animals aren't like that. Plants never talk about it. Insects abandon their cocoon and shed their skin without a whimper. No cicada ever goes whining on about the seven or fourteen years it had to spend beneath the blackened soil. Chirping jubilantly, they head straight off to reproduce, right up into the clear blue sky. Everything hunts, gallops, licks its own fur, basks in the sunlight, scatters flies with a shake of its tail, has a nest full of its own already clinging to the teats. Returns perchance (but then those are large, cumbersome creatures) to a spot where lies a pile of bleached bones, pauses, lows within the herd. Moves on again. Evolves, develops, mutates, becomes anomalous, unique. Improves its own chances of survival, scatters, builds fortifications, defences. Becomes a part of the great pandemonium. A glorious, unique and matchless—albeit highly eradicable—bit of diversity: zzzingzangzzoommmm . . .

All right, there may be beasts that are deranged, disturbed, delusional, just plain lazy. Human beasts of habit, their behaviour ingrained. Look, someone lays a hand low on someone's back or mons, and the thighs part obediently. Drably too, with all the dime-a-dozen cries, shouts, moans . . . Sometimes you can't hear the difference between one and the other, and in fact there's no difference to be heard . . . no matter what little cracks, cunts, bums, mouths . . . Everything can be borne in the end, the little hominoids know that too, and that is the most unbearable thing of all: the smile that never fades completely, a sort of serenity and resignation. The sweet hush money. Mars Bars, Snickers, Verkade chocolate. HEHH lines up the small change, the guilders and daalders before you on the steel desktop and, not much later, milk teeth already riddled with cavities are sinking greedily into thick layers of chocolate with nuts, raisins and caramel: mmmmmmmm-mmm.

And growing up oblivious, there is also the joy and the reassurance of the special, and of the commonplace. In winter a hot-water bottle in its woollen sock to turn round and round with glowing foot soles, soft flannel sheets, sunlight that makes your fingertips light up in a glow of reddish-orange. The hum of expectation (Frost flowers! Frost flowers on the windows!). A veil of white lace snaking soundlessly across a thin crust of snow. Drops of blood welling up from torn cuticles. Lovely black scabs to pick at. (Libby's voice: 'Will you help me make some clothes for my dress-up doll?') An extra blanket under which to fall asleep.

These days, after a meal perhaps a bit too copious, passing one's gaze over the naked body beneath the sheets, and the thought: look at that, white hairs already amid the frizzy pubes, how can that be?

And on awakening you hear the blackbird sing. A call to vengeance, or to reconciliation?

With you still trying the whole time to keep it all at arm's length, to strike a deal with the God scorned. 'Dear Lord, if you let Oleg live for a long, long time and don't tear us apart, so that I don't have to cross the savanna of the rest of my life all on my own and only have to reach out to find him in bed beside me . . . as long as I can press my backside against his stomach and then feel the soothing Pavlov reaction of his fingers tickling and caressing me (see here the patient and her caregiver) and that he may live long enough too, sweet Lord, so that when and if necessary, and I swear, truly only in the event of a definitive return of the primal fear (a fear that never goes away; the fall down the memory hole ends each time with a smack on the bottom of the old well, which really is one hell of a well!) he will be in a position to press and hold the pillow to the face—as long as that remains possible, dear Lord, I shall believe in Thee. And exalt Thy name and sing Thy praises. Melodramatically, subdued (at a high pitch or grunting like an animal rooting through thick underbrush . . .) as the Most Divine Vegetative and Unutterably Merciful of Plants.'

Alongside which: you yourself aren't fond of victims either. God almighty, they're so aggravating . . . and dull as the day is long, aren't they? With all that moaning and groaning . . . their bizarre exorcisms and antique fears that never go away completely? Get a life, you feel like shouting at them. Grab a broom, a shovel, a knife, a pair of scissors. Put together a little nest egg; after all, before long you'll be just as dead as the rest. Be merry, dance, party, try stuffing a candle up your butt. Eat a properly cooked risotto. Tend to your husband's penis; after all, he can't help it either.

Care for something or someone. Go forth and love. Feed your pet, be it dog or cat. Remember, they have no opposable thumb to open a can for themselves. Read a book, write a letter. Or sneak over to the emerald-green Chinese cabinet and take out the pair of delicate, curved shears with which you fantasize about the snip-snap-snip . . . even if that means snipping to pieces the safe dream you were planning to hide away in: he was a sweet man, old man, friendly man, considerate, not at all like the Minotaur that came in with his hot poker (stick it in, stick it in, stick the piggy on it and heat it up from the inside out).

Anna Alida: 'Goodness, child, you walk so strangely.'

'You walk weird,' they shout on the playground, and it's true. You *really do* walk weirdly. Butt clenched, tip, tip, tip on the tips of your toes . . . your locomotion is ludicrous, no doubt about it. When you're frightened or excited (in that lonely entanglement), the nocturnal port opens in deferential obeisance.

And you become a stink-spot.

*   *   *

But far more than being worried about all this shame-fulness, you're worked up about the aesthetics of it all. What are you supposed to do when you've become as vulgar, humdrum and banal as any goddam victim? Where the hell's the glory in that? You still have thoughts and dreams of your own, you know. Of a great escape. And you've got longings. To shake the clouds, like Thor or Odin, till the rain comes. To make something real, and at the same time less so. A story. Your kingdom for a solid, authentic story. One that's all thought up and imagined. Not the way you yourself have been imag-ined and thought up, though, the figment of somebody else's imagination. How to break free of this dog-chases-cat-chases-dog, sinking its teeth into its own tail for all time?

You think about becoming a murderer.

You think about becoming a necrophiliac. Really? Sure, why not? The dead need warmth and love too, just as much or maybe even more than the living. For starters, you're not easily shocked and don't readily find things mucky, filthy or disgusting. You've undergone suitable training to that end. Your pride was turned inside out long ago, and you're not inclined to think that things stink. You're familiar with the odour of decay, of course, but that has a certain warm, nigh-on motherly component to it. You can, for example (trained in such persistent fash-ion), imagine yourself going to the churchyard, opening the coffins and settling down beside your parents in all their present-day calm and serenity. Lying down beside them and keeping them company in their extremity and need while they, warm and covered with earth, get on with the full process of their decomposition. You could even touch their bellies, arms, legs, adjust their heads so they can rest more easily. You can think about things like that, feature them; they sound like the hurdy-gurdy of a lullaby . . .

You could lie with them (for a bit), oh yes.

You could read books to them, tell them stories, recite poems. You could watch a movie with them. Show them a movie. You could come to love them again and teach them how to love in return. They would be very quiet now. Hushed as children, perhaps.

And in the grass above you both, a humming, zooming and a ringing.

Yes, Henri Elias Henrikus Holbein annexed the territories Henne Fire, Toddiewoddie, Libby and yours truly. An act that may be seen as an affront of some consequence. (But how to avenge and respond to such an insult in a world which, as we've seen, has no tolerance for the rage of women?)

Perhaps better to save all this for Toddiewoddie's house. Her guest house. There and only there can we act as the Graeae, or Moirai as the Greeks call us, and share the one eye, one ear and one tooth we have between us. Convene the witches' sabbath and celebrate the feast of our unexpurgated rage.

Rage like a song of melting rock. Healing, beneficent rage. Yellow, gold and orange, bubbling to the surface like lava.

Teeming, glorious, majestic.

WITCHES' SABBATH (*GRAND GUIGNOL*)

T HERE WE HAVE them, in conclave at last, 170 years of age and more between the lot of them.

The first is on pills, the second builds towers of cigarette ash and complains about her pubic hair, which has grown 'hard as the bristles on a dog's back', the third chooses her wines judiciously.

'Fill that up for you?'

'Oh hell, why not?'

'A smoke?'

'A smoke!'

'My heart's pounding like a drum, you got another of those little yellow ones for me?'

So now down to business, what are we going to do with HEHH? the sisters twitter. Come on, who goes first?

'OK, what about spitting on his grave and jumping up and down on his headstone!'

Already *done* that, *did* that, *been there*!

Who's that, who was that? Is that Libby, little sissy-sister Libby, who watched so closely at Henri's wake to see his nasal organ turn all black and blue? (Should be quite dead by now, but let's wait a little bit longer, just to be sure . . .)

All right then, who's next? Aha, it's yours truly. A few bricks short of a full load, this one. Look at the way the tip of her tongue protrudes from between her lips, flickering with pleasure (for the first time in days, weeks, maybe even years) at the thought, the plan, the idea of being able to cut to pieces, limb by limb, body part by body part (with a Stanley knife, a box-cutter—and each and every time that magnificent click as a new blade slides into place, sharp and gleaming like a silverfish), to slice and to snipsnapsnip, thinner and finer all the while, until nothing is left of a certain HEHH but a few juicy strips of beef. Wait, no, not a Stanley knife, how about a little feminine couth and sophistication? What about a pair of nail scissors! Why yes, let's cut a lovely flower of flesh out of old Henri and fashion something new from him . . . starting with the leaves . . . the tongue and genitals don't necessarily need mutilating, only transplanted from the earth in which they took root. So let's make this a different kind of flower-bed, the scrotum pushed up inside the pelvis, the tongue frayed to a set of attractive, appealing corolla. All arranged with the utmost care and prudence (not perfectly symmetrical, more like real flower petals) around the stem or pistil which—depending upon the amount of sunlight, heat and care—hangs or grows in the middle . . . *maybe I'll breathe life into it again, the way I used to* . . . (this last bit spoken at a whisper). Mmmm, and snip away at whatever's left over, to make of it an organic work of art in harmony with its surroundings and at the same time somehow pleasing to the eye . . . that is my wish. Amen.

But is that enough? Is it sufficient? Oh no, no, no, this isn't nearly the kind of assurance the witches require. After all, there's still composition involved here, the semblance of some human form or other, or the intention of human flesh with inside it, there, the haemoglobin-rich fluid propelling it into motion—tapping, pushing, bending, sniffing, peeping, chewing, growling motion—and the making of decisions various and sundry. All the more refined and absolute by far, therefore, must the deconstruction be. Best, then, to slash or tear or dissect it to shreds, till nothing remains but a bit of mush or glop. No longer moving, only to be set in motion by the action of another.

And will the hexes then be content? Alas, even this is not enough. If they had their druthers, they would go on rending and tearing until rending and tearing is no longer feasible and no structure is left at all. But what then? What to do with that spray, that pulp of genetic material? Oh my dear Lord, sweet God, Allah, Odin, Jesus Christ and Zeus, so where would they take it then, and where could they leave it to be ab-so-lute-ly sure that no system would ever arise within it again?

No, that's not possible. But *that* (hear the whispers, see the grins), that is our desire.

'Amen.'
'Amen.'
'Amen.'

Toddiewoddie's macaroni always tasted like heaven to me, but today—with her room filled with our lionesses' roar—it is delicious beyond compare.

'Want to go out tonight?? No, I can't. I've got a date with my father.'

Hahaha. Hahaha.

(Thick Hague accent:) 'Hey, hey, you guys have that too? Sundays the old man with his pud out and a big glop of Nivea . . .? Oh yeah, but never on Tuesday. Nah, he musta been too tired then, on Tuesdays. Yeah, Tuesdays I bet he was shagged then.'

Hahaha. Hahaha.

Spam, she used spam in it, just like back then, tomato paste and Hero pearl onions. Atop the buffet, a (lavender) scented candle is smouldering in front of a photograph of Henne Fire. Henne is thirty-two in that picture. The other one, the terrible one showing her when she was already nothing but skin and bones, is in the top drawer, wrapped in tissue paper. ('Please, put that picture away, Toddie, please . . . don't ever show anybody that.')

Toddie tops up the glasses. Seventy she is, with plenty of her shoot-from-the-hip sexuality left to go around.

After a third glass of wine, yours truly launches rumbus-
tiously into an old tear-jerker.

> (*Incest*, the musical:)
> Aaaaand . . . their lives were one great vale of sorrow
> Their pa them most cruelly had shamed, O-lay!
> Their tender souls caught in the wringer
> Their little hearts mangled and maimed
> O-lay!

The intense pleasure we Graeae or Moirai derive from our
witches' game and our coven there in Toddie's two-room
flat is hard to describe, let alone summon up again. A
pleasure made even greater (and at the same time abridged)
by the fact that it's being played out in her Baba Yaga hut,
where no one can see us and our saliva can run freely.

Even though we have (in thought) totally and completely
annihilated HEHH ('*I'm* the one who runs things and *I'm*
the boss around here!' Heehee, *we're* the ones who run
things now, *we're* the boss), and even though Toddie and
Libby crease up with laughter when you say that her
house, Toddiewoddie's house that is, even back then with
psychopath "Toni" P. in it, remains in your memory the
warmest and safest of houses, compared to what of course,
but still a more pleasant, congenial and above all clearer
place, because you were at least allowed to wear your
glasses there during the day . . . despite all these things, the

thought still arises that perhaps none of this really suffices, and that we should carry out the execution all over again.

Ooooh, what is it then . . . what is it that we really want, anyway?

'Well . . . what about some luscious hunk, for a change . . . all the guys in this building act like they have a stick up their ass.' (Toddie)

'How about some money in the bank and a vacation for once, dammitalltofuckinhell!' (Libby)

And sixty thousand needles to stick under HEHH's fingernails. And a sheet of iron, to braise him slowly under . . .

But does everything always have to revolve around him, is that really necessary?

Such a little man.

Such an ordinary man.

Such a *dead* man.

There are, to be fair, a few daddy issues at play here.

But now that we're on the subject, now that he's the topic of the day, what is it with this sneaking off and lazing about in some hole in the ground somewhere? Isn't it about time his lordship woke up? Ah, now the hags are on a roll! Now the Holbein girls are in for some merriment!

(. . .)

The second bottle of wine does the rounds, the third's all ready to go. Courage enough has been summoned. In the seclusion of the hideaway hut on chicken legs, the disintegrating body of HEHH is dragged to the stand. Being dead is no excuse! Toddie sees to the clock, and sets the egg-timer. Libby holds the body in position. It's not a pleasant sight, but these women aren't easily shocked any more. All the honouring was done decades ago. The maggots and worms are flicked off of the corpse, the bones are pulled upright. Let the dead speak for himself. (He's going to need a lawyer, a defence attorney. Maybe one of the brothers Holbein will do that, Max or Kaj, if we were to grant them admission to a wingding like this one.) Good thing that we're limiting ourselves here to pure narrative; that means no actual stench, only the calmative distance of the written word. Because, to be perfectly frank, the dead are extremely lax when it comes to personal hygiene, to body odour. Even though HEHH in real life, I hasten to add, was the paragon of punctiliousness on that score! Always a handkerchief within reach. Bathed, barbered, shaved. Neat and tidy, in every nook and cranny.

The cross-examination begins . . . Quid pro quo, one thing in return for the other. Due process! The clock is set, the sand is poised in the hourglass. We'll spare him the hard light of day, the dead have no need for that.

Speak!

But: the dead man's tongue is grey, mouldy and swollen, and his twaddle is pretty much unintelligible . . . Such atrocious diction . . .! ('Unsatisfactory! Uses all the wrong words, is completely inarticulate, requires a speech therapist for the chattering of his teeth, or did he simply forget to put in his dentures?') No, it's no use. Not worth occupying our shared ear with, not worth seeing with our one eye (who's got the eye right now, anyway?), not ruminating over with our one tooth. Even though once he was such a crisply articulating and resolute teacher, each word falling like a cold pebble, the old Japanese water torture dripping on the forehead. (Great, make him listen! It's us talking now!)

What follows then: so much bitterness, such filthy language, such a rollicking!

(. . .)

No, listen to me now, lost are those who cannot forgive. Lost are those who can't even let a body go. All crimes in the end turn against the wronged and offended. Little in the way of sweetness or friendliness lives on in these hags. (And they were such sweet little dragonflies, what ever became of them?)

Look if you would at that pale, shuddering flesh, was that not once their father? And is this act of boundless vengeance and incrimination not an abomination on their part? Are these three wretched sisters, of whom I am one, not themselves an abomination? How little solicitude and tenderness is to be found in us. Like a set of carving knives, a triad of claws! Such lip!

Come now, counsel for the defence, trot out the list of his good deeds. (Look, there's this, and that, and that and thus and so.)

Our youngest brother, Kaj, weeping: 'He had his good points too!'

Suddenly the little girl with the gap between her front teeth steps to the fore and shakes her head, a tear dribbles down her cheek.

It wasn't like that, that's not how it went at all . . .!

For one single moment, our attention lags.

And then? Mayhem in the little apartment. The victim tries to escape, tries to cover his genitals (shame, shame): 'Lemme go, oooh, lemme go . . .'

He's knocked everything off the table, he hisses at us threateningly, spitting like an angry cat, his skin erupting in boils, pustules and sores.

Ear, eye and tooth? Our eye? Shrieking and groping around the room, we go after him.

'Get him, grab him. Stop him.'

The witches' sabbath. We really ought to do this again before long, next year maybe. Oh, next year for *sure*. (Toddie: 'Then we'll come to your place and we'll make a day of it again, then we'll eat your meatballs. Anyway, *I'll* eat them; you know they might be the last balls I ever put in my mouth.') Then it's home again, home again astride the broom-mobile, where we put on our disguises of writer, artist, housewife, single parent, senior citizen of modest means. Feline familiars? We've got those too. There goes Yevgeni, our tom, dingier, drabber now, he's been around the block a couple of times. Through the garden of Libby's little house along the dyke slinks another tom, Grijsje.

(Toddie: 'I've got a puss too, you know. I wouldn't want to neglect it, it needs looking after.')

Yes, apparently, we are content with our revenge. But that won't last long. The moment is fleeting.

Because there was a before-this. There is a before-this that does not go away.

At first the Minotaur was suckled by his mother. Only later was he fed human flesh and, deemed too dangerous for his surroundings, locked up in the labyrinth Daedalus designed especially for him. Without help, they said, those forced to enter it could never find their way back out.

*

Hurry, hurry, hurry, no room for delay . . .

In late 2015/early 2016, after our long, disconcerting stay in the den of winter and prompted by Henne's fall, when I began this investigation of our common but by the same token uncommunicable Holbein past which had so rudely come haunting the present (leaving me with no pleasure in life and the sense of having been squeezed out of the real world), I had no idea how complex and demanding a task I was taking on. I cannot deny that during this writing I have often been apprehensive. And still am, at times. The experiences I have described not only blunted my senses, but heightened them too upon my awakening. My hearing, in particular, became acute. For a time I heard all things in heaven and on earth—and a few things from hell as well: 'Papa, Papa, come and take away the monster that's waiting for me in the dark, it's hiding in the closet, it's sliding down the wall.' 'There's no such thing as monsters, dearie, only real people and their unbridled fantasy!'

What's more, I was afraid people would say I was insane. But even more, I feared that no one would say that, and so leave me with no means of escape. I know now that I was under a spell, one I've longed to fall back into at times, for it kept reality at bay.

Nor can I deny that it took me a great deal of time and effort to be able finally to think of this "Holbein-sein" as a malady, and to describe it as a tainted system. To do that, after all, I had to examine myself, and so become my own Petri dish. (I know now that I am a fairly accommodating person.)

In addition to which, it was my unspoken (writer's) wish to earn the seal of decency for our family. To present our story in such a way that we might emerge as proud possessors of fine qualities and characteristics. But, described from without, a discrepancy appears right away. An inner conflict and a vacillation. 'And why is that?' someone asks, someone who does not know us. Do we not enjoy many pursuits? Are we not blessed with many talents and a broad range of interests? Astronomy, physics, biology? Interests in Greek and Latin as well as mathematics (taken to include algebra and geometry). In natural philosophy, the fine art of chess, literature, cooking, painting, drawing ... Aren't we practical, technically minded, eclectically inclined? Do we not make up children's songs (*I'm a happy little louse, I live in a little girl's hair, in fact I do all my shopping there; I'm a happy, little Lou-ouse!*)? Are we not blessed with the talent to improvise, with black humour, self-mockery? This house has been endowed with gifts as well, has it not? So whence the fidgety legs, the fingers drumming on the tabletop, these eyes averted so quickly, these hands raised before the mouth, these bad teeth, these nocturnal wanderings or even the inability to sleep at all? These pale faces, loud voices and then suddenly this falling completely still? Why so skittish, so awkward and fearful almost of moving at all in select company? Or this Gilles de la Tourette-like syndrome of the foulest possible potty-mouthing? ('So I grab hold of the old snatch, the skank, and I give her the what-for!' 'Aaaah, my fuckin' crack itches so bad, I got monkey butt, sooo bad.' 'You want a bellybutton-lint sandwich, an earwax cupcake?'

Why this keeping ourselves and each other down, this regard for hardship as a near-virtue? (Libby: 'No, oh no, there's nothing I miss having, never have either. I can do without, get by on less, on nothing, really.') (Toddie: 'Oh, I wouldn't know about that, that's way over my head.') We've known ruthlessness, so what's with this sentimental outlook all the time? We can stand to see brains blown apart in zombie films or the havoc after a bombing attack, but not to watch children at play, not sick or injured birds or animals, not flowers wilting.

With increasing clarity, I see who we are. Heirs to a world of camouflage and (self) deception. The only thing I can figure is that it was this same old, worn-out deception that kept me from speaking up for such a long time. The way I lay motionless on the ground back in 2017, floored by a slipped disc, while this whole story churned inside me and gnawed and nibbled at my nerves and crawled up along my backbone like a rat.

What was I to do? After all, every choice I could possibly make seemed like betrayal, or an impossibility . . .

I thought about my brother, Max, the introverted locksmith of our childhood. Fourteen, fifteen, sixteen years old . . . on the tiled square among the rooftops on Damstraat, peering through his telescope at the stars and the moon (in an attempt to fathom the mystery of the universe, which is as much an enigma as we are). 'Wanna take a look?' he asks, picking up his four-, five-, six-year-old sister. After adjusting the lens a bit, the moon appears, like a gigantic skull in the night sky; a cool, pale-grey miracle.

He was a handsome young man, Alain-Delon handsome. Withdrawn. Quiet. The brilliant stable-boy, locked in his shed. The shield-bearer who played guitar wonderfully. The boy who could draw exquisitely. Beautiful girls in charcoal, round-breasted, narrow-hipped, their long hair swirling in the water: undines.

Many years later (when all the arrows have long been shot from the bow that quivered so tensely back then), he still waits at times, on perfectly silent nights, for that one special moment to show me, yours truly, and Oleg that which is ordinarily invisible. The rings of Saturn, Jupiter's moons. And through a rent in the night sky a glimmer of his boy's room, with the Salvador Dalí poster. *The Temptation of St Anthony*. Elephants on wispy insect legs bearing a coach, at its window a female torso roaring through time and space. Scattered on his bed the dog-eared SF paperbacks, Isaac Asimov (*I, Robot*) and Brian Aldiss (*Hothouse*). On his desk (right below the trap door that connects his musty alcove with the girls' room) a book lies open to grainy photos of that lonely moon in black and white, with her crevices and craters, her canyons and mountain tops.

I thought about Toddie:

'The world's a mean, nasty place, I'm telling you. We live in a really selfish world, nobody ever thinks about anybody except themselves; me first, last and always. You know, I wasn't counting on anything, and there was no reason for it anyway, but my son-in-law started in about it himself: "Toddie, today's your birthday. You're turning seventy. That's quite some accomplishment. Today's your birthday and the TV's busted, come on, we're going to buy a present, we're going out for a surprise." So he drives me down to MediaMarkt and has me pick out a TV; nothing too extravagant, I tell myself, not a really expensive one, this one's fine, I like this one, I say, and he says: is that the one, is that the one you'd go for? It's up to you, he says, but a bigger one's OK too, one with all the trimmings, and I think: here we go, now I'm getting a real gift, and I'm so surprised and I pick out a nice one, not too complicated with all that stuff on it, I don't care about that, but he says: go ahead, look around . . . and he pays for it and says: well, happy, happy birthday to you, a new TV for the two of us—and we drive back to his house and he gives me his old one.

'You know, sometimes I wonder whether the world's always been this cold, maybe it has. Keep your mouth shut, they say. Grin and bear it, honey catches more flies than vinegar. But what if I don't feel like it any more?

'Life is worthless, it's not worth a fucking hoot.

'The day the boy was born, I was wearing a navy-blue dress; a blue dress with a blue waistcoat. They put a tent over you, then they take the baby, and you don't see a thing.

'But he went to a good, respectable family, and I gave him his name.

'You know what still makes me cry a lot? My heart just breaks whenever I think about it . . . in 2014, when Henne got all gussied up and put on a pretty dress for her oldest kid's wedding party, and her ex, that fuckhead Niko with his new sourpuss girlfriend, just let her sit there the whole evening and never once asked her to dance, even though she was the mother of his children and they were married for twenty-five years, and they laughed at her too, because she hadn't shaved her legs.

'No, I don't think things are going to get any better. I think people are just bad and mean.'

And about Libby, who back in 2016 tossed all her primary-school notebooks and the diaries with their little locks (but inside them, nonetheless, the disapproving fountain-pen scratches of Henri Elias Henrikus Holbein: *Wrong! Not spelt correctly! This is not the way it is spelt!*) on to a roaring fire in her garden. The paintings of our Old Master stood lined up along the fence and went up in flames too. Max, who moved to Nieuwegein after his divorce and lives only a stone's throw away from her, helped her that day (his eyes, operated on only recently, tearing over the whole time: 'No, it's nothing, really, just a bit of dust'), shakily sawing the paintings for her into pieces (during his impoverished period, HEHH had painted on chipboard). All right then . . . on to the glowing coals they go.

About Ninny (whose real name is different, of course; a name that resembles that of the predator, *Mustela furo*, in its domesticated form): 'Listen, can I ask you somethin'? You guys got to tell me the truth: do you guys ever miss Papa and Mama?'

And about Kaj, so deeply sorrowful the day that we, Toddie, Libby and I, told him about our secret lives in the looking-glass.

It went on and on, pounding in my head: what are you doing? You're tearing down the house.

Still, it wasn't all bad . . .

There was the beautiful daughter, the big, grown-up child.

There was Oleg, travelling companion and *compañero*, who brought comfort and who, one gloomy November day (with yours truly in great need of livening up), saved a potato from the boil.

'We won't kill this one, he looks like a person. Look, here are his eyes, nose and mouth, he's smiling, he even has a navel!' Which was true, if you were prepared to squint a little.

Oh, and the fantastic adventures that potato had! We named him Jasper. How sweetly grew the runners from above and below the matchsticks we stuck (à la Funny Mister Potato Head) into the body, like a new set of arms raised to heaven. Oleg found him a perch in the big, overgrown citrus. There he waited amid the shadowy foliage, beneath the little orange fruits, until I came to pick him up for a photo shoot. (Jasper, blotto beside a hipflask of slivovitz. Standing behind the antique toy Fiat with larch-wood coffin on the roof—a memento from the TV programme *The Box*. Beside a pan of boiling water. As SM performer, with pearl necklace, fur and black mask. On a voyage through *Philip's Atlas of the World* (comprehensive edition). Hear the tropical birds, the cry of the yellow-crested cockatoo! In front of a photo of Caravaggio's Christ (*The Supper at Emmaus*), in "the tub" (a porcelain bowl in which I keep a rubber band and a few buttons). With a pen in the crook of one matchstick arm, and finally as an astronaut in an aluminium-foil spacesuit, in front of a picture of the Small Magellanic Cloud.

When he grew soft and wrinkly, Oleg laid him to earth in a planter on our balcony. In the summer the miracle took place, and we took and ate (Dear Lord, bless this food and shed your loving kindness upon Jasper, most merciful and gentle among thy tubers).

And in the evening, often, his hand . . . when he touches and caresses you, down your back . . . when he does that, mmmmmm, you grow calm . . .

Or playing with you, his fingers like a band of proud little soldiers marching, foraging, sometimes stopping, reflecting, hesitating . . . then advancing on the soft, blood-purple hills, lost in the hairs, caught, and under and slipping in, poking about, curious about that place (down the rabbit hole), plunging, sliding up and down, mmm-mmm, fulfilment coming like the darkness, go deeper, go harder, stronger, leave no room for anything else, mmmmmm, till the cock, the penis, the wang, the dong, the *Schwanz*, the rod, the velvet hunter, the stoat, the *kurac* explodes in a glorious mini-volcanic eruption of sperm and fluid. Feel the way it drips out and down your thighs, drip-drip (*don't worry, ooh, ooh ooh ooh oo-ooh ooh oo-ooh . . . don't worry, be happy* . . .). Strum down the smooth pebbles of his spine . . . such peace lying there beside you.

And while I'm writing this (with tiny stabs of the old back pain running through me) and wondering to myself who could possibly want to know about these events that were so strictly personal, so tied to a particular time and place, I burst out laughing.

Don't, I tell myself, flatter yourself by thinking that this story is in any way special or unique. No matter how peculiar, smutty or idiosyncratic in its specific details the story all of you share may be . . . that story is part of a convention. Even if it is of a strain that is withering on the vine, even if there aren't many families like that left any more. Meaning that you, all of you, belong to a clan that is almost extinct. The last of the Mohicans. A rare animal species, like the snow leopard or the white narwhal.

Then I laugh out loud again. Because there's so much idiocy in it. And such foolish and wayward folk.

About a year ago, I dreamt that my father had been turned into a raven and that we, Kaj, Libby, Max and I, had to bring him to the forest. (How that can be, when he had already been buried back in 2001? But I'm telling you—he had turned into a raven and we were bringing him to the forest.)

That night we never slept. The crowns of the trees formed an arbour under which we walked as we carried him. It was deathly still. The animals of the forest withdrew into the bushes. The birds concealed themselves amid the leaves and in the cracks of hollow trees. Only by lending a careful ear to the faintest sound could you hear a trembling. His breast was warmish. His beak, sharp and pointed (crafted by giants), of fine and ancient ivory. His plumage was crawling with king ants, gleaming purple in the morning light.

There, at the forest's edge, we laid him in the silt.

There, his long, thin spirit fanned out across the water.

Since then it is as though a fern has uncoiled inside me in the slowest motion: spreading exquisite pain, because this happens in deepest deepness. A frond, green, sturdy and pliant, touching everything inside me, unfurling now and releasing its age-old spores as I bend to the present.

There is growth, and there is movement.

Yes, glorious reptilian brain, remember how our life began on the glowing surface of the earth? The collision, the collaboration of the cells? Their lustful coitus, how they split and divided and multiplied . . .? How dark and green the giant ferns, like monstrous umbrellas? How huge, mesmerizing and terrifying the insects, with exoskeletons in the iridescent colours of metals and minerals yet to be discovered? How blue and transparent and vibrant, full of noise and whirring, the wings of the giant dragonflies?

These sounds from a world where everything just is and doesn't ponder over that "isness", where each sign is equal to itself. Where there is no taste of sweet, sour or bitter. And the only difference is the bit, the 0 and 1. The 1 meaning: nurturing life, and the 0: not nurturing. Where fire glows beneath ice, and the water is warm, lukewarm, green and turbid, with fish gliding through it, the way they're already longing to glide through air. Where we can feel our blood running, whether cold or hot . . . and nothing is metaphor, but all exists at once, both inside and outside of time, where falling is the same as flying.

Planets are not born, they burst violently into being.

SELECT BIBLIOGRAPHY

Ryunosuke Akutagawa, *Rashomon*

J.G. Frazer, *The Golden Bough: A Study in Magic and Religion*

Johann Wolfgang von Goethe, *Faust: A Tragedy*

Hendrik Jan Korterink, *Moordenaars in Nederland* (*Murderers in the Netherlands*), Bertram + de Leeuw, 2015.

Vladimir Nabokov, *Lectures on Literature* and *Speak, Memory*

Snorri Sturluson, *Edda*

SELECT BIBLIOGRAPHY

GENEALOGY

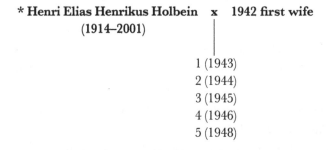

* Henri Elias Henrikus Holbein   x   1942 first wife
      (1914–2001)

1 (1943)
2 (1944)
3 (1945)
4 (1946)
5 (1948)

* Anna Alida Steiner   x   1945 first husband
      (1925–2005)

Henne (1946–2015) ('Henne Fire')
Toddie (1947) ('Toddiewoddie')

* Henri Elias Henrikus Holbein   x   1950 Anna Alida Steiner

F ('Ninny') (1951)
Max (1952)
Tobias ('Toby') (1956–1962)
MM ('Yours Truly') (1962)
Kaj (1963)
Libby (1967)